Structure in Architecture

PRENTICE-HALL, INC.   ENGLEWOOD CLIFFS, NEW JERSEY

Structure in Architecture

Mario Salvadori in collaboration with Robert Heller

PRENTICE-HALL INTERNATIONAL, INC.   London
PRENTICE-HALL OF AUSTRALIA, PTY., LTD.   Sydney
PRENTICE-HALL OF CANADA, LTD.   Toronto
PRENTICE-HALL OF JAPAN, INC.   Tokyo

Prentice-Hall International Series in Architecture

Mario Salvadori, Editor

SALVADORI AND HELLER   *Structure in Architecture*
SALVADORI AND LEVY   *Structural Design in Architecture*

Current printing (last digit):
14   13   12   11   10   9   8

"London Bridge is falling dow$_n$ . . ."

Foreword

In this thoughtfully written book, Professor Salvadori endeavors to eliminate one of the most serious gaps between theory and practice in the field of structures. His aim is to build a bridge between the more or less conscious intuition about structure, which is common to all mankind, and the scientific knowledge of structure, which gives a fair representation of physical reality on the basis of mathematical postulates.

No one doubts that the bridging of this gap is possible and that, if achieved, it would be extremely useful.

In order to invent a structure and to give it exact proportions, one must follow both the intuitive and the mathematical paths.

The great works of the distant past, built at a time when scientific theories were nonexistent, bear witness to the efficiency and power of intuition.

Modern theories are incessantly and progressively developed, and their refinement is illustrated by the construction of ever greater and more daring structures.

If structural invention is to allow the efficient solution of the new problems offered daily by the ever-growing activity in the field of construction, it must become a harmonious combination of our personal intuition and of an impersonal, objective, realistic and rigorous structural science.

In other words, theory must find in intuition a force capable of making formulas alive, more human and understanding, and of lessening their impersonal technical brittleness. On the other hand, formulas must give us the exact results necessary to obtain "the most with the least," since this is the ultimate goal of all human activities.

Through always clear and, at times, most elementary examples, Professor Salvadori's book tends to unify these two viewpoints (I was almost going to say, these two mentalities), which must be cast into a unique synthesis if they are to give birth to the essential unity of all great structures.

Future architects will find it particularly useful to study this book in depth and to meditate upon it, since even if they can entrust the final calculation of a structure to a specialist, they themselves must first be able to invent it and to give it correct proportions. Only then will a structure be born healthy, vital and, possibly, beautiful.

I feel that we must be particularly grateful to Professor Salvadori for undertaking this anything but easy task.

Pier Luigi Nervi

Preface

This book has been written for those

who love beautiful buildings and would like to know why they stand up;

who dream of designing beautiful buildings and would like them to stand up;

who have designed beautiful buildings and would like to know why they stood up.

The structural concepts presented in this book were introduced mathematically to the graduate students of the School of Architecture at Princeton University from 1955 to 1960, and to the graduate students of the School of Architecture at Columbia University from 1960 to date. Since 1961 the same concepts have been presented **without mathematics** to the freshmen in Architecture at Columbia with the help of the models and motion pictures of Robert Heller.

My deep gratitude goes

to my friend, colleague, and collaborator, Dr. Robert Heller, for his help in conceiving the illustrations and his constructive suggestions;

to my friend and associate, Paul Weidlinger, who acts as my structural conscience, and who read the manuscript;

to my students for their smiling acceptance of this "structural blast";

to my teachers at the Faculty of Pure Mathematics of the University of Rome, who made mathematics part of my mental makeup and allowed me at times to move beyond it;

to my friend and Dean, Charles R. Colbert, of the School of Architecture at Columbia for encouraging me to try this intuitive approach to structures;

to Mrs. Merle Guenther for her devotion and skill in typing the manuscript;

to Mr. Nicholas C. Romanelli and Mr. Robert Carola of Prentice-Hall for their interest in the design of this book, and their editorial help;

to Mr. Felix Cooper for drawing the illustrations;

to all my other friends who cannot be named here, for their interest and support during the brief but intense period of time during which the thoughts accumulated in years of study became this book.

New York, June 1962   Mario Salvadori

Contents

Structure in Architecture

Chapter One

Structure in Architecture

1.1 Historical Development

Structure is an essential component of architecture, and always has been. No matter whether man built a simple shelter for himself and his family or enclosed large spaces where hundreds could worship, trade, discuss politics, or be entertained, he has had to shape certain materials and use them in certain quantities to make his architecture stand up against the pull of the earth and other dangerous loads. Wind, lightning, earthquakes, and fires had to be resisted, if possible, with expenditures of labor and materials that were not unreasonable in relation to their availability. And because from earliest times a sense of beauty has been innate in man, all construction was also conceived according to certain esthetic tenets, which would often impose on the structure far more stringent requirements than those of strength and economy.

It may be thought, therefore, that structure has always been considered important, and, in a sense, has dictated architecture. This is simply not so. Magnificent buildings have been created in the past, and are created even today, with a notable disregard for the correctness of structure. The Parthenon, divinely beautiful as it is, translates into marble structural forms typical of wood construction and is, structurally speaking, "wrong." In fact, wood is a material capable of withstanding tension, and horizontal elements, requiring both tensile and compressive resistance, are well built out of wood. Stone withstands only compression, and horizontal elements can be built in stone only by reducing their length and supporting them on heavy vertical elements, such as columns or pillars. Hence horizontal elements of stone are incorrect. On the other hand, Gothic cathedrals could span up to one hundred and cover hundreds of square yards crowded with worshippers by making use of the arch, a curved structural element in which tension is not developed. Thus stone is the correct material for a vaulted type of structure, and the beauty of the Gothic cathedrals satisfies both our esthetic sense and our feeling for structural strength.

It has been argued by some architectural historians, as well as by some structural engineers, that a deep concern for structure will unavoidably lead to beauty. It is undeniable that a "correct" structure satisfies the eye of even the most unknowledgeable layman, and that a "wrong" structure is often offensively ugly. But it would be hard to prove that esthetics are essentially dependent on structure. It is easy to show, instead, that some "incorrect" structures are lovely, while some "correct" ones are esthetically unsatisfying. It may perhaps be wiser to say that correctness of structure is, most of the time, a necessary condition of beauty, but is not sufficient to guarantee beauty. Some contemporary architects and engineers, such as Felix Candela and Pier Luigi Nervi, are so imbued with artistic sense that their structures are beautiful. But some grandiose buildings, recently constructed by the use of daring engineering techniques, undeniably lack beauty.

We may thus conclude that a knowledge of structures on the part of the architect is, to say the least, highly desirable, and that correctness of structure cannot but add to the beauty of architecture.

1.2 The Present Interest in Architecture

In the recent as well as the ancient past, the figure of the architect was unique: he was an artist and a technologist, a designer and a builder. Michelangelo could be a painter, a sculptor, an architect, and a master builder: Saint Peter's in Rome bears his imprint in all four fields. During the last half-century, instead, specialization of knowledge has taken over the field of architecture, and the various functions, once to be found in the same man, are now exercised by different men. Two men are essential in the construction of any important building: the architect and the civil engineer. Today, no architect would dare design a building of even modest size without consulting a structural engineer. The roots of this dependence are to be found in the increasing importance of economic factors, in the technological direction of our culture, and above all, in our mass civilization's need for large structures.

While the number of humans has multiplied at an increasing rate during the last few centuries, so as to create a "population explosion," civilized societies have been giving each human more services, sharply increasing the "psychological density" of the population. Each one of us requires, and is given, more schooling, more travel, more medical care, more entertainment. The mass media allow, and compel, large numbers of people to gather under the same roof for all the gregarious activities so typical of our era. Large stations, large stadia, large theaters, large churches, large arenas appear in increasing numbers. Urban agglomerations require the sprouting of taller buildings. The large structure has become a symbol of our culture and a monument to its groups, be they governments, churches, or corporations.

The architect is challenged by these tremendous themes; the layman becomes aware of the importance of architecture in his own life. Thus, in a healthy climate of public interest, the specialists meet to solve new, difficult problems, and cannot ignore the impact of their work on the general public. The general public, whose moneys are often used for these large buildings, takes a personal interest in their construction. This interaction between the specialists and the public may lead to better, and more correct, architecture, provided the layman understands the basic problems of the specialist, and the specialists themselves have a common bond of mutual understanding. This is the central theme of contemporary architectural education, including both the education of the architect and the popularization of architecture.

1.3 The Architect and the Engineer

Today, every architect and every architectural student is convinced of the importance of structural knowledge, but the acquisition of such knowledge is more difficult than expected. The rapid development of construction techniques based on the use of new materials (such as aluminum, or reinforced and prestressed concrete), as well as the mathematical difficulties inherent in the design of new structural forms (such as large roofs of all shapes) make it almost impossible for a man with an essentially artistic background to even grasp the potentialities of the new methods of design and construction. The contemporary architect, perhaps the last humanist of our time, must be conversant with esthetics, engineering, sociology, economics, and, generally, with planning. Instead, under the influence of tradition, he is often trained primarily as an artist. His familiarity with the basic tools necessary to an understanding of modern technology is, most of the time, limited: mathematics, physics, and chemistry are not essential subjects in his curriculum.

On the other hand, the knowledge of the engineer in the fields of sociology, esthetics, and planning is as limited as that of the architect in technical subjects. A dialogue between the architect and the engineer becomes practically impossible: they lack a common vocabulary.

Since this dialogue is necessary, one may wonder, at first, whether the engineer should become more of an architect or the architect more of an engineer.

But little thought is required to realize why it is mainly up to the architect to bridge the gap. The architect is the leader of the construction team; the engineer is just one of its members. The architect has the responsibility and the glory, the engineer but a service to render, creative as it may be.

In view of the increasing interest in architecture shown by the public at large, is it possible to give both the architect and the public an understanding of the structural facets of the engineering problem? Is this possible without a thorough indoctrination in higher mathematics, physics, and economics? In other words, can the essentials of structural action be understood by an intelligent person untrained in the mathematical and physical sciences?

The answers to the questions above are all in the affirmative if a clear distinction is made between an understanding of basic structural concepts and a thorough knowledge of structural analysis.

1.4 Structures and Intuition

It is obvious that only the most serious training in mathematics and the physical sciences will allow a designer to analyze a complex structure to the degree of refinement required by modern technology. Today's structural engineer is a specialist among specialists, a subgroup among civil engineers. As new technologies develop, even structuralists specialize: at present some structural engineers specialize in reinforced concrete, others specialize in reinforced concrete roofs only, and some in roofs of only one particular shape. One goes to these specialists for advice on a particular type of structure, as one would go to a medical specialist for advice on a rare type of disease.

But it is just as obvious that, once the basic principles of structural analysis have been established, it does not take a specialist to understand them on a purely physical basis. We all have some familiarity with structures in our daily lives: we know at what angle to set a ladder so that it will carry our weight, and whether the plank over the brook will give in as we walk on it. We know whether our rope is strong enough to lift a pail of water from the bottom of a

8

well, and whether the tent pitched at camp will be blown away by the wind. It is but a fairly easy step to capitalize on these experiences, to systematize such knowledge, and to reach an understanding of how and why a modern structure works.

The layman may find this inquiry fascinating. The architect will find it mandatory: without it he will soon be out of the field of contemporary architecture. For the interested public it may be one more hobby; for the architectural student and the practicing architect it is one of the basic requirements of their profession.

Once he has grasped the fundamentals, the architect must become conversant with the more refined points of the theory of structures. This will allow him to apply intelligently a wealth of new ideas and methods unavailable until a few years ago even to the greatest architects.

There is an obvious danger in this new availability and freedom. Art is enhanced by limitations, and freedom may easily lead to anarchy. Since today almost any structure can be built, the architect is less hampered by technological difficulties and may be led astray into the world of the most unjustifiable structures. It is true that the average contemporary architect can aspire to greater achievements in the field of structures than was possible for the exceptional practitioner only a hundred years ago, but such achievements are the fruit not only of technology but of "blood, sweat, and tears."

What follows is an attempt to introduce the reader to the field of structures without appealing to a formal knowledge of mathematics or physics. This does not imply that structures will be treated in an elementary, incomplete, or simplified manner. On the contrary, some of the structural concepts presented in the last chapters of this book are refined and complex; nonetheless, they can be grasped by the reader and recognized in general architectural situations on a purely intuitive basis. This better knowledge of structural action will lead the interested student to a readier understanding of the finer points of structural design.

Chapter Two

Loads on Structures

2.1 The Purpose of Structure

Structures are always built for a definite purpose. This utilitarian element is one of the essential differences between structure and sculpture: there is no structure for structure's sake.

Structure's main purpose is to enclose and define a space, although, at times, a structure is built to connect two points, as in the case of bridges and elevators, or to withstand the action of natural forces, as in the case of dams or retaining walls.

Architectural structures, in particular, enclose and define a space in order to make it useful for a particular function. Their usefulness stems, generally, from the total or partial separation of the defined space from the weather, and may not require its complete enclosure: the cantilevered roof of a stadium stand protects the spectators from the weather without enclosing them in a space (Fig. 2.1).

The enclosed space may serve many different purposes: the protection of the family, the manufacture of industrial products, the worship of deity, the entertainment of citizens, the gathering of lawmakers. Different purposes, served by different spaces, require different structures, but all structures, by the simple fact of their existence, are submitted to and must resist a variety of loads. Only in rare cases is resistance to loads the primary purpose of a structure: loads are, usually, a necessary and unavoidable evil.

municipal
Florence stadium 1929-32   see Nervi p18

2.1 Partial protection from weather.

2.2 Loads

The determination of the loads acting on a structure is a complex problem. The nature of the loads varies essentially with the design, the materials, and the location of the structure. Loading conditions on the same structure may change from time to time, or may change rapidly with time.

The most important loads carried by an architectural structure do not change rapidly with time: they are called **static,** and are the basis for the design of the structure.

In order to simplify the checking of structural strength, the loads most commonly encountered in practice are not evaluated case by case, but are suggested, and even dictated, to the designer by rules and regulations contained in codes. The load to be carried by the floor of a building varies so much, depending on the occupant of the floor, the distribution of furniture, the weight of machines, or the storage of goods, that codes substitute for it an **equivalent load.** This equivalent load is derived, on the basis of statistical evidence, for given types of buildings, and is modified from time to time as new conditions arise.

The equivalent load must be such that under the **worst** circumstances the floor will not fail, nor deflect so much as to become unusable. The code load must, therefore, be a **multiple** of the load that could produce the

14

failure or the unacceptable deflection: the greater the uncertainty about the actual load, the greater the multiple adopted in the codes.

Code loads are **conventional loads:** a floor load may be assumed to be a constant number of pounds on each square foot of floor, even though, in practice, no floor is ever loaded uniformly. Similarly, the pressure exerted on a building by the wind may be assumed to be constant in time and distributed uniformly over its surface. The wind, instead, blows in gusts, and wind pressure varies from point to point of a building. Here again, the code simplifies the design procedure by taking the wind variations into account statistically, and suggesting "safe" conventional wind pressures.

Whenever the loads on a building are not considered by codes, and when they present characteristics that may endanger a structure's life, they must be accurately determined through experiments or by mathematical calculations. The effect of hurricane winds on a skyscraper may have to be found by means of aerodynamic tests on a model, conducted in a wind tunnel.

It is not always sufficient for the designer to consider only code loads, since the responsibility for the strength of the design rests with him and not with the code authorities; this is particularly true in circumstances where code regulations do not apply. It is therefore essential for the architect to acquire an awareness of loads.

2.3 **Dead Load**

The unavoidable weight of the structure itself, and the weight of all loads permanently on it constitute its **dead load** (Fig. 2.2). It is one of the paradoxes of structural design that one must know the dead load beforehand in order to design the structure, while it cannot be determined until the structure is designed. The dimensions of a structural element depend essentially on the loads acting on it, and one of these loads is the dead load, which in turn depends on the dimensions of the element. The designer is compelled to start the calculation of a structure by **guessing** its dimensions and, hence, its dead load. He then adds to it all the other loads, checks its strength, and finds out at the very end of the calculation whether his guess was correct. Long practice alone will prevent innumerable wrong guesses in structural design. The checking of structural strength for given loads, called **structural analysis,** is a fairly routine operation. The initial educated guess, called **structural design,** must come from experience and is often the result of an almost artistic intuition rather than of scientific calculations.

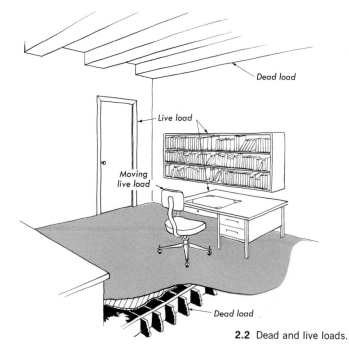

2.2 Dead and live loads.

The dead load is, in many cases, the most important load on a structure. It may, by large factors, outweigh all other loads, particularly in large structures and in those built of heavy materials. In bridges, in roofs over wide unencumbered areas (halls, churches, theaters), in stone and masonry structures of a massive type (columns, buttresses) the dead load often dictates the dimensions of the resisting elements. In certain cases the dead load is not only important, but useful or even essential—as, for example, in a gravity dam, where it is used to resist the pressure of water.

Modern structural materials, such as high-strength steel, reinforced concrete, or aluminum, in some cases reduce the importance of the dead load in relation to the other loads, but in no case can the dead load be ignored. Its main characteristic is its continuous presence: it is a **permanent load.**

The dead load is easily computed. Once the dimensions of the structure have been determined on the basis of prior experience, its weight is evaluated by consulting tables of unit weights for structural materials. One thus finds that the average weight of concrete varies from 100 to 150 pounds per cubic foot, the weight of steel is 490 pounds per cubic foot, and the weight of aluminum one-third that of steel, while wood weighs, as an average, 30 pounds per cubic foot, and brick 120 pounds per cubic foot.

The difference in unit weight of the various materials influences the dimensions of structural elements, but it will be seen later that the essential factor in deciding the efficiency of a structural material is the ratio of unit weight to strength.

18

Although there are few uncertainties about the dead load, its calculation is a painstaking and tedious job. It is also a fundamental job, since the amount of materials used in a structure is, together with labor, one of the major components of its cost.

2.4 Live Loads

All loads other than the dead load of the structure are called **live loads** (Fig. 2.2). They include all the **movable weights** to be carried: humans and animals, machines and fixtures, partitions and other nonstructural elements, rain, snow, and ice. The pressure or suction of wind, the pressure of water, and the push of earth are also included among the live loads.

It was noticed above that many of these loads are of such an uncertain nature as to require "averages" to be established by code writers. Thus, according to the New York Building Code the live load on the floor of an apartment building is to be assumed equal to an even load of 40 pounds per square foot, while the live load on the floor of a storage house is to be taken as 120 pounds per square foot. Even partitions, which act on a small floor area, are to be distributed over the entire floor in view of the uncertainty of their locations: they are considered as a load of 10 to 50 pounds per square foot, depending on their type and number.

The weight of snow depends on the climate of the region where the building is to be erected: according to codes, it is equivalent to 60 pounds per square foot in Northern Canada, and to 40 pounds per square foot in New York City.

2.3 Wind load.

The wind load on a building is difficult to ascertain with any degree of accuracy, because it depends on the wind velocity **and** on the shape and surface of the building (Fig. 2.3). Average wind velocities are known with some degree of certainty, but it is practically impossible to measure the highest instantaneous velocity of a hurricane wind, or to forecast the largest velocity the wind will have in a certain locality. The influence of the building itself presents even greater uncertainties: its shape may produce either pressures or suctions, and the roughness of its surface may change the value of the local pressures. In any case, codes prescribe safe, even pressures or suctions due to wind; these are revised from time to time in order to take into account the knowledge continuously accumulated in the field of aerodynamics. The dynamic action of wind loads will be considered in Section 2.6.

The dead load and other vertical loads due to the pull of the earth are resisted by suitable structural systems. Wind pressures and suctions and other horizontal loads require, at times, a different structural system for their absorption. Horizontal wind-bracing systems may be seen on the underside of bridges (Fig. 2.4), while vertical wind-bracing systems are usually hidden within the walls of most buildings (Fig. 2.5).

20

2.4 Horizontal wind-bracing system.

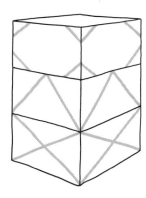

2.5 Vertical wind-bracing systems.

2.5 Thermal and Settlement Loads

All structures are exposed to temperature changes, and change shape and dimensions during the cycle of day and night temperatures, and the longer cycle of summer and winter temperatures. The effects of changes in dimensions due to thermal expansion and contraction are often equivalent to large loads, which may be particularly dangerous because invisible. A simple example of this type of loading condition will suffice to indicate its nature and importance.

A steel bridge spans 300 feet over a river (Fig. 2.6); it was built in winter, while the average temperature was 35 degrees Fahrenheit. On a hot summer day the air temperature reaches 95 degrees Fahrenheit, and the bridge expands, because it acquires the temperature of the surrounding air. The increase in length of the bridge, which may be calculated to be only 1.3 inches, is small compared to its original length. But if the bridge piers make it impossible for this elongation to take place, they must develop in the bridge a horizontal compressive load capable of reducing the length to its winter value (Fig. 2.6). Since steel is very tough in compression, it takes a large compressive load to reduce the length of the bridge by 1.3 inches: this load is so high that it would use up **half the strength of the steel.** The obvious way of eliminating such an overload is to **allow** the bridge to change its length with varying temperatures. This is usually done by supporting one of the bridge ends on a ''rocker'' (Fig. 2.7).

22

2.6 Thermal load.

2.7 Rocker support.

A similar condition of thermal expansion, with different but equally danger-ous consequences, is encountered in large domes. When the external tem-perature increases or decreases, the dome tends to expand or contract. Since it is usually prevented from so doing by its underground supports, which remain at a constant temperature, it will move mostly up or down: the dome "breathes" (Fig. 2.8). The top of a dome covering a glass enclosed hall and spanning 200 feet may breathe up and down as much as 3 inches due to temperature changes, and if the glass walls follow this movement the panes break. A special type of sliding support eliminates this danger.

More complicated thermal loads are developed in a dome during the daily ther-mal cycle, when one of its sides is heated more than the other. The dome changes shape in an unsymmetrical fashion and becomes distorted (Fig. 2.9). The stresses due to this distortion may be high and are difficult to evaluate.

These simple examples show that a structure is particularly sensitive to ther-mal changes if by the nature of its shape, support conditions, and materials it tends to **restrain** the changes in dimensions due to temperature. On the other hand, satisfactory displacement under loads requires a structure to be stiff. Hence, the requirements for stiffness and for thermal loads are con-tradictory. Whenever a structure is to withstand heavy loads and small temperature changes, it may be made quite stiff. Whenever it must withstand large temperature changes and relatively small loads, it **must** be made flexible in order to accommodate such changes: the structure successfully resists this loading condition by giving in rather than by fighting it.

24

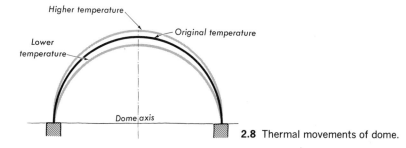

Higher temperature

Original temperature

Lower temperature

Dome axis

2.8 Thermal movements of dome.

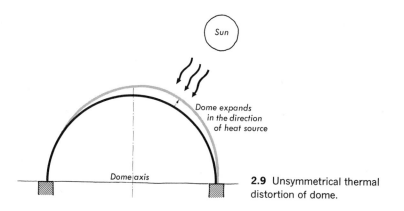

Sun

Dome expands in the direction of heat source

Dome axis

2.9 Unsymmetrical thermal distortion of dome.

Another condition, producing effects equivalent to those of high loads, may stem from the uneven settlements of the foundations of a building. A soil of uneven resistance, loaded by the weight of a building, may subside more in a specific portion of the foundation than in others. The soil deflections reduce the support of the foundation in certain areas, and the portion of the building above them either shears off the rest of the building [Fig. 2.10(a)] or hangs partially from it [Fig. 2.10(b)]. No additional load has been applied to the building by the uneven settlement, but the supported portion of the building carries more load, and of a different type, than it was designed for. The unsupported section of the building is also under strain, as can be seen from the deflection of its beams [Fig. 2.10(b)].

Thermal and settlement stresses are examples of a category of stresses due to deflections rather than loads. An example of a stressed but unloaded structure may be built by cutting a piece out of a ring and welding the ring again so that it looks untampered with. If cut, this ring snaps open, demonstrating the stress "locked" in it. A similar condition may be found in some rolled steel beams. If one of these beams is cut down the middle with a saw, its two halves open up and curve in opposite directions, indicating a certain amount of stress locked in by the rolling process (Fig. 2.11). One of these beams might fail under load, because the stresses produced by the loads are superimposed on the "locked-in" stresses and exceed safe values. Locked-in stresses are put to good use in **prestressed** and **post-tensioned** reinforced-concrete structures (see Section 3.3) and other prestressed structures (see Sections 11.1 and 12.14).

26

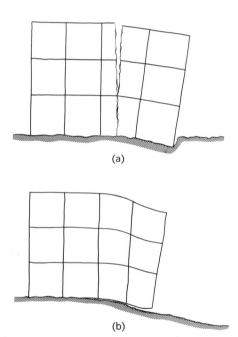

(a)

(b)

2.10 Uneven settlements of foundation.

2.11 Locked-in stresses.

2.6 Dynamic Loads

All the loads considered in the preceding section were assumed not to change or, at least, to change slowly with time: they are said to act **statically.** In codes even the wind is assumed to act "statically," although it obviously does not.

Loads that change rapidly, or are applied suddenly, are called **dynamic loads.** They can be exceptionally dangerous if ignored; consequently, their action must be clearly understood.

The common experience of driving a nail by giving it a hammer blow indicates that the sudden application of the hammer weight achieves results unobtainable by the slow application of the same weight.

In order to ring a heavy church bell, the sexton yanks its rope rhythmically; the bell swings progressively further until eventually it rings. The sexton could not achieve this result by exerting a sudden hard pull on the rope: he must, instead, "swing" rhythmically for a while (Fig. 2.12).

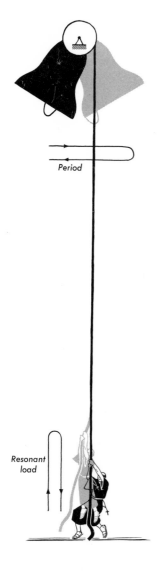

Period

Resonant
load

2.12 Resonant load.

The force exerted by a hammer blow is called an **impact load;** the rhythmic pull of the sexton a **resonant load.** In the first instance, the higher the velocity of the hammer or the shorter the time of application of the load, the greater the effect: an instantaneous blow produces an extremely high force with possibly shattering results. In the second, a relatively small force applied "in swing" for a long time produces increasing effects: a small "in-swing" force of a few pounds may eventually turn over a bell weighing several tons.

Dynamic loads are exerted on structures in a variety of ways. A sudden gust of wind is similar to a hammer blow. A company of soldiers marching "in step" exerts a resonant load on a bridge, when their step is in rhythm with the oscillations of the bridge. Some small bridges have collapsed under such resonant loads.

An impact load is characterized by a very short time of load application; resonant loads by their rhythmic variations. But when is an impact time "short"? And when is a varying load "in resonance" with a structure?

All structures are, to a certain extent, elastic. They have the property of deflecting under loads, and of returning to their initial position once the loads are lifted. As a consequence of their "elasticity," structures have a tendency

30

to oscillate: a skyscraper swings after the passing of a wind gust, and a railroad bridge oscillates up and down after the passage of a train. The time required for a structure to go through a complete swing, or up-and-down oscillation, is called its **fundamental period.** In order to go through a complete swing a modern building will take anywhere from one-tenth of a second to 6 or more seconds. A stiff structure oscillates rapidly: a low, rigid building has a short period. A flexible structure oscillates slowly: a tall steel skyscraper may take over 6 seconds for a complete swing. The fundamental period of a structure is, in fact, a good measure of its stiffness.

The time of application of a load is measured against the fundamental period of the structure: if this time is **short** in comparison with the fundamental period, the load has **dynamic** effects; if **long,** the load has only **static** effects. It is thus seen that the same load, applied over the same time, may be static for a given structure and dynamic for another. A wind gust on a stiff building of short period will have the same effect as a constant pressure. A wind gust on a flexible building may strain the structure to a much greater extent than its static pressure would lead one to predict. The blast of a nuclear bomb reaches its peak pressure so rapidly that its effects are always dynamic. Its destructive capacity is a dramatic example of what dynamic loads can do to a structure.

In a variety of practical cases the dynamic effects of a load are 100 per cent larger than its static effects. If a one-pound load is put slowly on the plate of a spring scale, the scale hand will stop at the one-pound mark on the dial. If the same load is placed on the plate suddenly, the hand will move to the two-pound mark and then oscillate, stopping eventually at the one-pound mark (Fig. 2.13).

Most of the loads applied to architectural structures do not have impact characteristics, except those due to earthquakes. An earthquake is a jerky motion of the ground. This series of randomly variable jerks is transmitted to a building through its foundations, and produces much larger jerky motions of the higher building floors (Fig. 2.14). Inasmuch as earthquakes are unpredictable, and their action on a building depends on the structural characteristics of the building itself, earthquake design is a complex chapter of structural theory. It is only in the last few years that enough information on earthquake motions and on dynamic building characteristics has been gathered to allow safe, simplified calculations based on "equivalent static loads." Tall buildings thus correctly designed have survived earthquakes that destroyed smaller, inadequate buildings.

2.13 Dynamic load.

2.14 Earthquake motions.

Resonant loads occur at times in architectural structures. A piece of heavy machinery may vibrate because of the motion of its parts. If this vibration has a period equal to that of the supporting structure, the vibrations of the machine will be transmitted to the structure, which will swing with increasing oscillations. Floors, foundations, and entire buildings may thus be endangered by rather modest loads with a resonant period.

More complicated dynamic phenomena are due to the wind. If a scarf is held out of the window of a moving car, it oscillates rapidly up and down. This "flutter," produced by the constant rush of wind on the scarf, is called an **aerodynamic oscillation.** The reader may produce such an oscillation by blowing against the edge of a thin piece of paper. Aerodynamic oscillations were produced by a wind of constant and fairly low velocity blowing for six consecutive hours against the suspension bridge at Tacoma, Washington; the oscillations increased steadily in magnitude, twisting and bending the bridge, until it collapsed (Fig. 2.15).

Dynamic wind loads on a structure are also created by its deflection of the wind stream. This explains, for example, the dynamic overpressures measured on the windward side of a building, which may blow windowpanes **in.** Underpressures or suctions, measured on the leeward sides of buildings, may blow windowpanes **out.**

All dynamic phenomena are complex. The designer must be aware of their action, and use with circumspection even the "equivalent static loads" suggested by codes.

34

2.15 Aerodynamic oscillations.

Chapter Three

Structural Materials

3.1 The Essential Properties of Structural Materials

A large variety of materials is used in architectural structures: stone and masonry, wood, steel, aluminum, reinforced and prestressed concrete, plastics. They all have in common certain essential properties that suit them to withstand loads.

Whether the loads act on a structure permanently, intermittently, or only briefly, the deformation of the structure (a) must not increase indefinitely, and (b) must disappear after the action of the loads ends.

A material whose deformation vanishes rapidly with the disappearance of the loads is said to behave **elastically** (Fig. 3.1). All structural materials are elastic, to a certain extent. If they were not, and a residual deformation were present in the structure after unloading, new loadings would usually increase the residual deformation, and the structure would eventually become useless. On the other hand, no structural material is perfectly elastic: depending on the type of structure and the nature of the loads, **permanent** deformations are unavoidable whenever the loads exceed certain values. Hence, the loads must be limited to values that will not produce appreciable permanent deformations: structural materials are usually stressed within their so-called **elastic range.**

Most structural materials are not only elastic but, within limits, **linearly elastic:** their deformation is proportional to the load. Thus, if a linearly elastic beam deflects one-tenth of an inch under a vertical load of 10 tons, it will deflect two-tenths of an inch under a 20-ton load (Fig. 3.2). Most structural materials are used, almost exclusively, in their linearly elastic range.

Materials presenting permanent deformations after the disappearance of the loads are said to behave **plastically** (Fig. 3.3). All structural materials behave plastically above their elastic range: the load at which a material starts behaving in a clearly plastic fashion is called its **yield load** or yield point.

38

3.1 Elastic behavior.

3.2 Linearly elastic behavior.

3.3 Plastic behavior.

Although large permanent deformations are to be avoided, it must not be thought that plastic behavior above the elastic range makes a material unsuitable for structural purposes: in fact, the opposite is true. For example, while the material is in the linearly elastic range, its deformations increase at the same rate as the loads. Above the yield point, deformations increase more rapidly than the loads, and eventually keep increasing even if the loads are **not** increased. This **flow** or **yield** under constant loads is thus the clearest sign, and a good warning, that failure is imminent. Other structural advantages of plastic behavior will be considered in subsequent sections.

Materials to be used for structural purposes are chosen so as to behave elastically in the environmental conditions and under the type of loads to be expected during the life of the structure. The importance of this requirement can be illustrated by a simple example. If a wax candle is improperly inserted in a candlestick, the seemingly stiff candle will slowly bend out of shape at room temperature, and after a few weeks may be completely bent over (Fig. 3.4). This deformation would occur much more rapidly in an oven, while in a refrigerator it might be indefinitely limited. Under arctic conditions wax is "more structural" than in the tropics.

Given a sufficiently long time, a candle deforms under its own weight, but if one tries to bend it quickly, it breaks; it becomes **brittle.** All structural materials exhibit a similar behavior: at low temperatures and under fast load applications they are elastic and brittle; at high temperatures and under long-time loads they "flow." The temperature and time required for flow differ for different materials.

40

3.4 Material flow.

Materials that are linearly elastic up to failure (Fig. 3.5), such as glass and some plastics (note the misnomer), are highly unsuitable for structural purposes. They cannot give warning of approaching failure; moreover, they often have a brittle behavior and shatter under impact (Fig. 3.6).

Steel at normal temperatures has a useful linearly elastic range followed by a plastic range, but becomes suddenly brittle at a temperature of minus 30 degrees Fahrenheit. Some unexpected failures of steel bridges in Canada have been traced to this sudden transition from elastic-plastic to brittle behavior at low temperature. At high temperatures even steel, one of the strongest structural materials, loses most of its strength: it flows at 700 degrees Fahrenheit. If steel is to be used safely in construction it must be fireproofed; reinforced concrete is fireproof, provided the reinforcing steel is sufficiently protected by a cover of concrete.

Some materials have a relatively limited elastic range and behave plastically under low loads. Some plastics (thus correctly named) flow under almost **any** load. The yielding behavior of these plastics, and the brittle behavior of others, makes most of them unsuitable, so far, for structural purposes. But reinforced plastics, such as Fiberglass, present acceptable structural characteristics, and their increased use is easily foreseeable.

Modern structural materials, such as steel, are **isotropic:** their resistance does not depend on the direction in which they are stressed. Wood, on the other hand, has different strengths in the direction of the grain and at right angles to it. This drawback is remedied by joining, with plastic glues, sheets of wood with grains in different directions. The plywood thus obtained presents more homogeneous strength characteristics, and moreover can be made weather resistant.

42

3.5 Brittle behavior.

3.6 Brittle failure.

Structural materials can also be classified according to the kind of basic stresses they can withstand: tension, compression, and shear (see Chapter 5). Tension is the kind of stress that pulls apart the particles of the material [Fig. 3.7(a)]. Compression pushes the particles one against the other [Fig. 3.7(b)]. Shear tends to make the particles slide, as they do in a wire sheared by a pair of pliers [Fig. 3.7(c)].

All structural materials can develop compressive stresses. Some, such as steel, stand compressive and tensile stresses equally well. Others, such as stone or concrete, do not: their use is necessarily limited to loads and shapes that will not develop tensile stresses. Materials capable of resisting tensile stresses usually resist shearing stresses also; essentially compressive materials, on the other hand, do not have high shear strength (see Section 5.3).

3.2 Material Constants and Safety Factors

For structural purposes, materials are mostly used within their linearly elastic range, and this implies that their deformations are proportional to the loads upon them. But different materials deflect differently under the same loads. If a steel wire 5 feet long, 1/16 inch in diameter, is loaded by a weight of 1000 pounds, it lengthens by 2/3 inch; the same wire made of aluminum stretches three times as much, that is, 2 inches (Fig. 3.8).

Steel is tougher than aluminum in tension. The measure of this toughness is a property of each structural material, called its tensile **elastic modulus.** The elastic modulus is the force theoretically capable of stretching a wire 1 square inch in area to twice its original length (theoretically, because in actuality the wire will break before stretching that much). The elastic modulus of steel is 30 million pounds per square inch; the modulus of aluminum is 10 million pounds per square inch.

44

(a)

(b)

(c)

Cross-section view

3.7 Basic stresses.

Steel

Aluminum

5 ft

1000 lb

1000 lb

1000 lb

1000 lb

2/3 in.

2 in.

3.8 Tensile deformations.

The modulus in compression differs, in general, from the modulus in tension. The compressive modulus of concrete is found to be, as an average, 3 million pounds per square inch; its tensile modulus has little significance, since its tensile strength is negligible. The compressive modulus of wood is 1 million pounds per square inch in the direction of the fibers, and 3/4 million pounds per square inch at right angles to them. Steel and aluminum have the same modulus in tension and compression.

For purposes of safety a knowledge of the stress at which a material will start yielding is of the utmost importance. The average yield point in tension or compression for steel and for aluminum is 50 thousand pounds per square inch. Since structures cannot be allowed to yield under loads, lest their permanent deformations accumulate in time, safe stresses are usually assumed as a fraction of the yield point. Thus, steel and aluminum may be safely stressed in tension or compression to about 20 to 30 thousand pounds per square inch, and concrete to approximately 1000 pounds per square inch in compression. The **safety factors** thus introduced depend on a variety of conditions: the uniformity of the material, its yield and strength properties, the type of stress developed, the permanency and certainty of the loads, the purpose of the building. This last factor is of great importance from a social viewpoint: the safety of a large hall is more critical than the safety of a one-family house, and must be evaluated more conservatively. Factors of safety for buildings of exceptional dimensions, to be occupied simultaneously by large numbers of people, are established today so as to make it **most improbable** that even a predetermined, small number of

46

persons will be killed by structural failure during the life of the structure. The calculation of such safety factors involves the use of probability theory, and leads to results that can, and must, be gauged in terms of human lives.

Safety factors cannot be established on the basis of the yield point whenever the material does not present a well-defined yield point, or does not have any. The first case occurs with concrete, which does not have a clear transition from elastic to plastic behavior; the second with brittle materials, which behave linearly up to failure. In these cases safety must be measured directly against failure, as far as the material is concerned. It is thus important to realize that steel will break in tension at a stress of 70 to 200 thousand pounds per square inch, and concrete in compression at a stress of 3 to 8 thousand pounds per square inch. These stresses are called the **ultimate strength** of the material.

But some advantage may be had in establishing safety factors on the basis of failure, even when the yield point is clearly defined. These safety factors give direct information on the overload the structure can support **before it collapses,** rather than on the overload that will make the structure unusable because of excessive deformation. A knowledge of both overloads may be useful in establishing higher safety factors for permanent and semipermanent loads on the basis of yield, and lower safety factors for exceptional loads (hurricane winds, earthquakes) on the basis of failure. This criterion is accepted by most codes: a combination of normal vertical loads and of exceptional lateral loads (such as wind or earthquake forces) is usually allowed to stress the structure 33 per cent above the stresses due to vertical loads only.

3.3 Modern Artificial Materials

Iron has been used as a structural material for thousands of years, mainly in combination with other materials. Since the tensile properties of iron and the compressive properties of wood were well known, a combination of wood struts and iron tie-rods was used in the trusses spanning the naves of medieval churches (Fig. 3.9).

Increased knowledge in metallurgy, chemistry, and physics has substantially improved the properties of structural materials during the last 100 years. Stainless steel has eliminated the danger of rust. Ultimate tensile stresses of steel alloys have reached as high as 200 thousand pounds per square inch, and those of steel "whiskers" recently manufactured have reached millions of pounds per square inch, forecasting revolutionary developments in steel design. Similarly, some new aluminum alloys have the strength of structural steel and are one-third as heavy. Plastic glues have transformed wood into a permanent, practically isotropic material. Glass-reinforced plastic combine the strength of glass with the nonbrittle behavior of plastics.

48

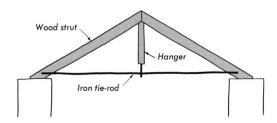

Wood strut

Hanger

Iron tie-rod

3.9 Wood-and-iron truss.

Possibly the most interesting of the new structural materials is reinforced concrete. Combining the compressive strength of concrete with the tensile strength of steel (see Section 5.4), this material can be poured in a variety of forms, so as to adapt itself to the structure and the loads at hand. A new freedom in the design of structures has thus been acquired, far greater than that inherent in assembling beams and columns of standard shape, like those of rolled steel sections. The reinforcing steel, like a web of tensile tendons, pervades and holds together the mass of cement, sand, gravel, and water, which sets and hardens to make the structure a single, monolithic entity.

The properties of steel depend on the careful check of ore mixtures and furnace temperatures at the steel mill. The properties of concrete depend on the quality and amounts of components in the mixture. Concrete is so sensitive to variations in mixture that it must be carefully and scientifically "designed" in specialized laboratories for use in large construction projects. Each batch of concrete used on the job is then tested to guarantee that its composition is in agreement with the laboratory design. The grain size distribution of the sand and gravel aggregates, the quality of the cement, and the quantity of water used may substantially affect the concrete strength and its hardening time. During the "setting" process heat is produced, and unless

50

the concrete is properly cured, i.e., protected from both low and high temperatures, it may set improperly and crack, or have an ultimate strength lower than its design strength. These shrinkage cracks may permit humidity and water to reach the reinforcing steel, which rusts and eventually disintegrates.

The manufacture of concrete is a delicate process, requiring as much care as that of any chemical. The concrete for important construction jobs is seldom mixed at the site; it is manufactured in concrete plants and transported there. On the other hand, because concrete properties vary so much with composition and methods of mixture, many different types of concrete can be obtained, each suited for a specific purpose. Concrete with a compressive strength as high as 8000 pounds per square inch, rapidly hardening concrete, and concrete with lightweight aggregates, are consistently manufactured. The reader will appreciate the potentialities of this new material after becoming acquainted with some of its applications to daring structural systems.

Prestressed concrete further advances the basic concept of a tensile reinforcement for a nontensile material. Tendons of exceptionally strong piano wire are stretched through the concrete and pulled against the entire concrete mass, which is compressed by the tension of the tendons. An unloaded beam of prestressed concrete seems unstrained, but "locked-in" stresses compress the concrete and tense the steel. The tension developed in the beam by the loads (see Chapter 7) reduces, or at the most wipes out, the initial concrete compression so that the concrete is never in tension, nor does it tend to crack (Fig. 3.10). The prestressing (in compression) of a concrete member was proposed by the very first investigators of reinforced concrete. Unfortunately, no steel available at the time (the end of the nineteenth century) had a yield point high enough to allow the tendons to remain tensed after the initial flow of the concrete. Only during the last three or four decades has high-strength steel, suitable for this purpose, been manufactured at reasonable prices, making prestressed concrete a reality.

"Ferro-cemento," a structural material invented and successfully used by Nervi, is a combination of steel mesh and cement mortar. In Ferro-cemento (iron concrete) a number of layers of wire mesh, with square holes less than half an inch on a side, are placed parallel and close together across the thickness of thin elements and embedded in a mortar of cement and sand (Fig. 3.11). The resulting material has the compressive capacity of an excellent concrete and the tensile elasticity of steel, since the steel is distributed through the mortar so as to hold the mortar particles together even when tension is applied to the element.

Finally, one may mention that the high compressive strength of ceramic tile may be combined with the tensile strength of steel and the cohesive properties of concrete to create a material similar in behavior to reinforced concrete. Torroja, among others, has shown how imaginatively one may use such material in countries where steel is prohibitively expensive and labor costs are low.

The proper use of structural materials is essential to correct design, since available materials limit the choice of structural systems in all important problems.

52

(a)

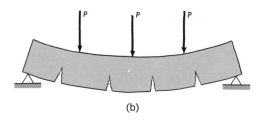

(b)

3.10 Prestressed concrete beam.

3.11 Ferro-cemento.

Chapter Four

Structural Requirements

4.1 Basic Requirements

Modern developments in materials production, construction techniques, and methods of analysis have introduced new freedoms in architectural design, considerably widening its scope. Subsequent chapters will illustrate the results achieved in this field, describing and analyzing the most commonly used structural systems of contemporary architecture.

These new freedoms do not exempt modern structures from satisfying certain basic requirements which have always been the foundations of good architecture, and which may be listed under the following headings: equilibrium, stability, strength, functionality, economy, and esthetics.

4.2 Equilibrium

The fundamental requirement of equilibrium is concerned with the guarantee that a building, or any of its parts, will not move. Obviously, this requirement cannot be strictly enforced, and some motion is both unavoidable and necessary; but the displacements allowable in a building are usually so small compared to its dimensions that to the naked eye the building appears immovable and undeformed.

Certain elementary conditions that will insure the equilibrium of particularly simple structures can be easily visualized. An elevator hanging from a cable is supported by the pull of the cable; the cable, in turn, hangs from the pulley at the top of the building. If the elevator weighs one thousand pounds, and is at rest, the cable will exert on the elevator a pull of a thousand pounds. The weight of the elevator and the pull of the cable are equal and "balance out": the elevator is "in equilibrium" (Fig. 4.1). Two boys pulling on a rope with equal forces do not move: the rope is in equilibrium (Fig. 4.2). But if one of the boys exerts a greater pull than the other, he will yank his friend from his stand, and both the boys and the cable will move: equilibrium is lost. Similarly,

56

4.1 Equilibrium of vertical forces.

4.2 Equilibrium of horizontal forces.

if a statue weighing one thousand pounds is set on a column, the column exerts an upward push of one thousand pounds on the statue (Fig. 4.3). If the column exerted a smaller upward push, the statue would move down, and there would be lack of equilibrium.

These elementary examples show that a body does **not** move in a certain direction if the forces applied to it in that direction balance out: a force exerted in a given direction must be opposed by an equal force exerted in the opposite direction. Whenever this happens we say that there is **equilibrium in that direction.**

A slightly more complicated situation is presented by the equilibrium in the vertical direction of a bridge when a locomotive is crossing it. The bridge rests on piers at its two ends and its weight will be neglected. When the locomotive is at midspan each pier supports half the weight of the locomotive: the weight of the locomotive is "equilibrated" by two equal "support reactions" [Fig. 4.4(a)]. When the locomotive is just entering the bridge from the left, its weight is supported almost entirely by the left pier. As the locomotive moves across the bridge the reaction of the left pier decreases and the reaction of the right pier increases [Fig. 4.4(b)], until they become equal when the locomotive is at midspan. From then on, the right pier reaction increases and the left decreases, until the right pier carries the entire weight of the locomotive as the locomotive is just leaving the bridge [Fig. 4.4(c)]. The bridge transfers to the piers the weight of the locomotive, whatever its position: to have vertical equilibrium the two reactions must **always add up** to this weight, but the reactions differ in value depending on the weight's location.

58

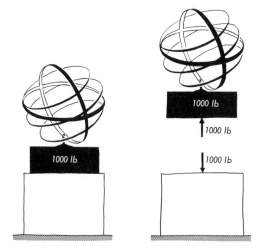

4.3 Equilibrium of vertical forces.

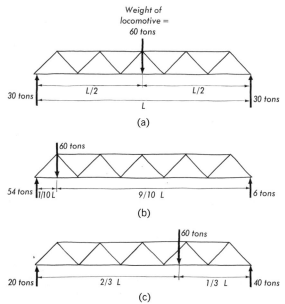

4.4 Bridge reactions.

Another familiar equilibrium situation is illustrated by two boys of **identical** weight sitting at the end of a seesaw with **equal** arms. The support of the seesaw "equilibrates vertically" the weights of the two boys, and "reacts" with an upward push equal to their combined weight [Fig. 4.5(a)]. Equilibrium breaks down when the boys sit at different distances from the point of support: the seesaw **rotates** in the direction of the boy sitting farther away from the point of support [Fig. 4.5(b)]. Such distances from points of support are called "lever arms." In order to guarantee "equilibrium in rotation" the weight and the lever arms of the two boys must be the same. If the two boys have different weights, equilibrium in rotation can still be obtained by giving the lighter boy a larger lever arm, and the heavier boy a smaller lever arm. In fact, **equilibrium in rotation** requires that the weight **times** the lever arm of each boy have the same value [Fig. 4.5(c)].

Such simple equilibrium principles will be found to apply to all structures. Equal and opposite forces will guarantee equilibrium in a given direction, and equal and opposite products of forces and lever arms will guarantee equilibrium in rotation.

The first applications of equilibrium are found in the study of the next structural requirement: stability.

60

4.5 Equilibrium in rotation.

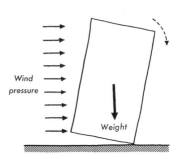

4.6 Instability due to wind.

4.3 **Stability**

The requirement of "rigid-body" **stability** is concerned with the danger of unacceptable motions of the building **as a whole.** When a tall building is acted upon by a hurricane wind, and is not properly rooted in the ground or balanced by its own weight, it may topple over without disintegrating (Fig. 4.6). The building is **unstable** in rotation. This is particularly true of tall, narrow buildings, as one may prove by blowing on a slim cardboard box, resting on a rough surface (lest it should slide).

The danger of rotational instability is also present when a building is not "well balanced" and is supported on a soil of uneven resistance. If the soil under the building settles unevenly, the building may rotate, as the Leaning Tower of Pisa still does, and may eventually topple over (Fig. 4.7).

A building erected on the side of a steep hill may, by its own weight, have a tendency to slide down its slope. This may happen either because the building skids on the soil, or because a layer of soil adheres to the foundations and slides on an adjoining layer (Fig. 4.8). The second occurrence is not uncommon in clay soils when water seeps through the ground, transforming the clay into a soapy material.

62

4.7 Instability due to uneven settlement.

(a)

Clay

Rock

(b)

4.8 Instability due to sliding.

All these cases of instability are related to the soil, and to the building foundations. From the viewpoint of economy and usage foundations are a "necessary evil"; moreover, they are out of sight so that the layman is seldom aware of their importance and cost. For example, the foundations of a heavy structure erected on loose sand permeated by water must allow the building to "float" on such a soil: they are built by means of "rafts" which in structure are similar to the hull of a ship (Fig. 4.9).

Elaborate precautions against soil failures are extensively taken to guarantee the stability of structures. Piles can be driven into the soil to depths which permit the building to be supported by friction against the surface of the piles or to reach solid rock (Fig. 4.10). The piles may be rammed into the soil or may be made to slide into it by rapid vibrations. Soils may also be consolidated by chemical means. Usually, an improvement of soil conditions accompanies the design of proper foundations, but soil mechanics is as yet a difficult and uncertain art; to this day, most of the damage to buildings comes from faulty foundations, even though their cost may reach 10 per cent, or more, of the total cost of the building.

4.9 Raft foundation.

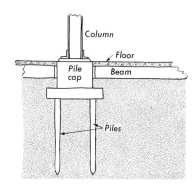

4.10 Foundation on piles.

4.4 Strength

The requirement of strength is concerned with the integrity of the structure and of each of its parts under any and all possible loads. To this purpose, the structural system is first chosen, and the loads on it are established; the state of stress is then determined at significant points of the structure and compared with the kind and amount of stress the material can safely stand. Factors of safety of varying magnitude are used to take into account uncertainties in loading conditions and material properties (see Section 3.2).

Rigidity should not be confused with strength: two structures may be equally safe, even though one deflects more than the other under the same loads. Although it is often a measure of strength against loads, rigidity may be a sign of weakness in a structure subjected to temperature changes, uneven settlements, and dynamic loads (see Sections 2.5 and 2.6).

Certain structural weaknesses may lead to modest damage, while others may produce the collapse of the structure. Hence, the designer must check strength under a **variety** of loading conditions to obtain the **worst** stress situation at significant points of the structure. The structural optimist is inclined to believe that a structure collapses only if faulty design is compounded with faulty construction, and helped by an act of God. The cautious pessimist believes, instead, that structures collapse at the slightest provocation. In practice, structures do collapse, although in small numbers; moreover, owing to the plastic behavior of structural materials (see Section 3.1), most collapses do not occur suddenly, and they seldom take human lives.

The strength of a structure is often evaluated according to the rules and regulations of codes. These procedures are usually safe, but may become uneconomical when they ignore recently developed techniques and materials.

The responsibility for strength rests squarely on the shoulders of the structural engineer. Every day his job is made more complex, and safer, by the increased theoretical knowledge and the improved tools at his disposal. Among the new tools, the electronic computer deserves special mention. These "electronic brains" allow the performance of otherwise impossibly lengthy calculations in a matter of a few seconds or minutes, and are particularly useful in the kind of basic calculation to be performed daily by the structural engineer. In fact, the electronic computer has already supplanted the engineer in lengthy routine calculations, but at the same time has done much more than that.

The possibility of repeating a long calculation in a matter of minutes allows the consideration of a variety of combinations of shapes, sizes, and materials, and the choice of "the best" among a number of designs. Computers have thus brought about the "partial optimalization" of structural problems, which until a short time ago was no more than theoretically possible.

Moreover, the computer permits a more accurate analysis of problems of exceptional complexity—for example, those connected with earthquake design. Before the advent of the computer the rigorous analysis of such problems cost so much, in both time and money, that approximate solutions were mandatory, involving wasteful use of materials. Today large savings and greater safety are obtained by the more detailed and realistic studies computers make possible.

When the mathematical analysis of an exceptionally difficult problem cannot be carried through rapidly and economically, the designer may solve the problem by means of a test on a structural model of the building. The construction of a reduced-scale model requires a thorough knowledge of material properties, of appropriate scale ratios for lengths and thicknesses (which usually differ), and of correct scale ratios for static and dynamic loads. A number of laboratories, properly staffed and equipped for structural model testing, exist in the world today: dams, large domes, and other exceptional structures are often designed on the basis of their tests.

In the rare cases in which doubts may exist even about the reliability of a model test, the engineer may decide to test a full-scale structural member. This procedure is usually adopted when an important component, appearing repeatedly in a structure, does not lend itself to a clear analysis. It is a costly and time-consuming method, and though it yields incontrovertible information on the behavior of a structural element, it is seldom resorted to.

4.5 Functionality

Structural functionality is concerned with the influences of the working structure on the purposes for which the building is erected. For example, floors could be economically built by giving them curvature, as in the dome of a church: their thickness and their cost would be greatly reduced. But, since the pull of gravity is vertical, floors must be horizontal.

Suspension bridges are flexible structures. The Golden Gate Bridge in San Francisco sways as much as thirteen feet under strong wind gusts. Such motions obviously must be limited, not only so that fast-traveling cars are not swayed from their paths, but also because the pressure of a steady wind produces aerodynamic oscillations capable of destroying a bridge if it is too flexible (see Section 2.6).

The excessive flexibility of a structure may impair its functionality, if the deflections under static loads make it difficult or uncomfortable for people to move in it. Aluminum, which is three times as flexible as steel, in many cases requires **design for deflection** rather than for strength. Worse conditions may arise under resonant loads: a stream of traffic may produce a continuous and uncomfortable vibration throughout a structure, seriously impairing its usefulness. Buildings over subway or railroad tracks are often supported by lead insulation pads to stop such vibrations.

4.6 Economy

Economy is not always a requirement of architecture. Some buildings are erected for monumental or symbolic purposes: to aggrandize the owners in the eye of the public, or to enhance spiritual values. Monuments to the state or to "corporate images" fall in the first category; churches belong in the second. Their cost has little relation to their financial value.

But the utilitarian character of structure is so fundamental that even the structural systems of nonutilitarian buildings are influenced by economy. In other words, a strict structural budget must always be contended with unless the structure **itself** is an advertising display: an aluminum structure may be required, regardless of cost, in order to emphasize the ownership of the building by an aluminum manufacturer.

In the great majority of cases the structural engineer is expected to make comparative cost studies and, other things being equal, to choose the most economical structure. In a modern building other engineering costs, particularly those concerning mechanical systems (heating, air conditioning, electrical, and plumbing), far outweigh structural costs. The cost of the structure is usually less than 20 to 30 per cent of the entire cost of a building. Hence, even a substantial reduction in structural costs seldom represents a saving of more than a small fraction of total building costs.

In establishing structural costs, one must consider the cost of structural design: this represents only 1 to 2 per cent of total building costs. The moneys allotted to structural design are subdivided into a budget for the preliminary design, in which the system is established, and one for the final design, which includes preparation of the working drawings, checking of the shop drawings prepared by the contractor, and, sometimes, inspection or complete supervision during construction. Final drawings are elaborate pieces of workmanship, and may cost from $1000 to $2000 apiece.

The two largest cost components of a structure are materials and labor. In this connection, two basic types of economy are encountered in the world today. In the first, usually found in the most advanced industrial countries, the cost of materials is relatively low and the cost of labor relatively high. In the second, usually encountered in less developed or underdeveloped countries, this ratio is reversed.

The solution of the structural problem is influenced in a fundamental way by the ratio of materials to labor costs. In the first type of economy, all kinds of machinery (cranes, conveyors, excavators, compressors, electrical tools) are used to reduce labor costs and to speed construction; easily assembled, prefabricated elements are the rule; steel is often the typical material. In the second, labor is used in large amounts for both transportation and construction; small elements are employed to minimize the use of heavy equipment; masonry, brick, and concrete are typical materials.

70

Continuous changes in productivity and economic balance introduce a variety of intermediate conditions, depending on location and time. Concrete is becoming more favored and more competitive in countries where steel reigned until a few years ago. Metallic structures are becoming popular in countries where, up till now, concrete has been the most economical material.

The availability of heavy equipment is one of the main limits upon the use of large prefabricated elements in construction. Some of the most interesting work done in Europe is conceived with basic elements not exceeding the capacity of the most readily available cranes, which is of a few tons. On the other hand, elements weighing tens of tons are commonly used in the United States in construction jobs handled by small contractors.

Availability of skilled manpower limits methods of construction in a variety of ways. The use of Nervi's Ferro-cemento is not economical in the United States, because the pouring of cement mortar between the superimposed wire meshes must be performed by hand (see Section 3.3). Cement guns cannot be adopted in this case, because the velocity with which the mortar is ejected makes it bounce off the meshes. Most of the delicate stone work typical of medieval buildings is ruled out today by the lack of stone masons, whose tradition of apprenticeship has vanished. Similarly, a shortage of specialized welders may make it impossible to consider an otherwise economical steel structure. Even a lack of equipment to test the execution of the delicate welded joints may rule out such a solution.

Other more subtle factors may also decisively influence cost. At times, the regulations of local codes tip the economic balance in favor of a specific material by imposing restrictions on another. For example, certain codes limit the thickness of flat concrete slabs to no less than a given value. The application of this regulation to curved slabs, which structurally could be much thinner, may make uneconomical the construction of a small reinforced-concrete dome. The inadmissibility of aluminum as a structural material is typical of the limitations imposed by certain codes.

Fire regulations may favor concrete because of its fire-resistant properties, and comparative fire insurance costs may just as decisively recommend this material.

The initial cost of a structure is but one factor in its economy: maintenance is another. The low maintenance costs of concrete and aluminum structures may swing the balance in their favor, when compared with that of steel structures.

Speed of construction influences the amount of loan interests to be paid during the unproductive building period, and is another factor to be considered in the choice of a structural system. Prefabricated elements, whatever their material, allow simultaneous work on foundations and superstructure, and shorten construction time; hence, they are becoming increasingly popular. Governing bodies and labor unions have at times retarded or accelerated the adoption of modern structural systems. Political conditions have had the same effects.

Economy in structure is obtained through the interplay of numerous and varied factors: the designer and the contractor must be relied upon to weigh them carefully in order to develop the most appropriate method of construction for each set of conditions.

4.7 Esthetics

The influence of esthetics on structure cannot be denied: by imposing his esthetic tenets on the engineer, the architect often puts essential limitations on the structural system. In actuality, the architect himself suggests the system he believes best adapted to express his conception of the building, and the engineer is seldom in a position to change radically the architect's proposal.

72

In some cases the architect consults with the engineer from the very beginning of his design, and the engineer participates in the conception of the work, making structure an integral part of architectural expression. The balance of goals and means thus achieved is bound to produce a better structure and a more satisfying architecture.

The influence of structure on architecture and, in particular, on esthetics is more debatable. It was remarked in Section 1.1 that a totally sincere and honest structure is conducive to esthetic results, but that some architects are inclined to ignore structure altogether as a factor in architectural esthetics. Both schools of thought may be correct in their conclusions, provided their tenets be limited to certain fields of architectural practice. No one can doubt that in the design of a relatively small building the importance of structure is limited, and that esthetic results may be achieved by forcing the structure in uneconomical and even irrational ways. At one extreme, the architect will feel free to "sculpt" and thus to create architectural forms inherently weak from a structural viewpoint, although realizable.

At the other end of the scale, exceptionally large buildings are so dependent on structure that the structural system itself is the expression of their archi- tecture. Here, an incorrect approach to structure, a lack of complete sincerity, a misuse of materials or construction methods may definitely impair the beauty of the finished building.

The influence of structure on modern architecture is so prevalent that some architects wonder whether the engineer may not eventually take over the field of architectural design. The growing importance of technical services and of structure suggests such a danger. And a grave danger it would be, since the engineer, as a technician, is not trained to solve the all-encompassing problems of architectural design. But these fears may, after all, be unjustified: the engineer, while participating creatively in the design process, knows that in a group society like ours his role is limited to a collaboration with the leader of the group. This leader is and will always be the architect.

4.8 Optimal Structures

A discussion of the basic requirements of structures leads naturally to the question of whether one can satisfy all these requirements and obtain "the best structure" for a given architectural problem.

To answer the question we should first clarify "for whom" the structure is to be best. For the owner it should, probably, be the least expensive. For labor it should employ the most man-hours. For the supplier of a specific material the best structure should use that material in large quantities. For the structural engineer it might be the easiest to analyze, the most interesting to study, or the most daring, depending on whether he is more interested in profit, theoretical skill, or personal satisfaction and fame.

From the viewpoint of the basic requirements considered in the previous sections, the best structure may be the most stable, the strongest, the most functional, the most economical, or the most beautiful.

Thus it is obvious that the question of establishing the "best" structure does not have a simple, single answer. On the other hand, one may strive for the best structure under a number of specific limitations. For example, optimal solutions have been established in aeronautical engineering under the assumption that minimum weight is the **only** criterion by which structural elements ought to be judged. Similarly, the standard rolled wide flange (W₣) and I-sections, which are basic elements in all steel structures, have been studied geometrically to approach maximum strength per unit weight when used as beams or as columns (the two shapes are geometrically different).

One may establish more general criteria for "the best" column by considering a variety of shapes and materials, and by comparing costs. But it soon becomes apparent that the large number of factors in even the simplest problem of this kind makes it practically impossible to establish the values of these factors leading to an optimal solution. The column, one of the simplest structural elements, may have a variety of shapes (square, round, I-shaped, boxed); each shape may have a variety of sides-, or radii-ratios; the thickness of each side may be different; the length of the column may be large or small compared to its lateral dimensions; the column may be supported on a foundation, or be one of a series of superimposed vertical columns; the materials to choose from may be many; the load to be supported by the column may be centered, or off center. It is understandable that a group of structural specialists has been at work for over 20 years in the United States in order to establish simple criteria of strength and design for columns of steel and aluminum.

A question of common concern is the determination of the "lightest structural system," which supposedly spans the "longest distance" with the "minimum weight" of materials. Even considering a single material, simple studies show that different structural systems do not vary in weight as much as one may believe. The weight saved by the use of certain structural elements is often found to be required in their connections. Sometimes a system appears lighter than others, until a check of its flexibility shows that additional material is needed to stiffen it and make it functional.

The evolution of structural systems is a slow and delicate process. This should not discourage the serious student from investigating new possibilities, or the practicing engineer from adopting new techniques. Let them simply beware that a field as old and tried as Structures does not bear new fruits without the lavishment of incomparably more labor than that required by a routine application of established principles.

Chapter Five

Basic States of Stress

5.1 Simple Tension

Structures deform whenever loaded. Although these deformations can seldom be seen by the naked eye, the corresponding stresses have measurable values. Stress patterns may be quite complex; each, however, consists at most of only three basic states of stress: tension, compression, and shear.

Tension is the state of stress in which the particles of the material tend to be pulled apart. The steel cables lifting or lowering an elevator have their particles pulled apart by the weight of the elevator (see Fig. 4.1). Under the pull of the weight the cables become longer: lengthening is typical of tension. The elongation of a **unit length** of cable is called its **tensile strain** (Fig. 5.1).

Provided the material is not stressed beyond its elastic range (see Section 3.1), the lengthening of the cable depends only on its cross section, its length, and the load. The larger the diameter of the cable, the smaller the unit elongation: the tensile strain is proportional to the load carried by each unit area of the cable cross section, or the **tensile stress** in the cable (Fig. 5.2). The ratio of tensile stress to tensile strain is a characteristic of the material called its **elastic modulus** in tension (see Section 3.2).

For a given strain the lengthening of the cable is proportional to the length of the cable: if the cable elongates by 1/4 inch when the elevator is at the top floor of an eight-story building, the cable will elongate 2 inches when the elevator is at the ground floor (Fig. 5.3).

78

5.1 Tensile strain.

5.2 Tensile stress.

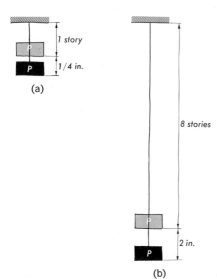

(a)

(b)   **5.3** Tensile elongation.

Certain materials, such as concrete, may be easily torn apart by tension; others, such as steel, are very strong in tension. A high-strength steel cable, one square inch in area (1.2 inches in diameter) can safely carry a load of 100,000 pounds, and will break only under a load of 200,000 pounds or more. Since the unit weight of steel is 3/10 pound per cubic inch, this cable could hang up to a length of 300,000 inches, or about 5-1/4 miles, without snapping. A cable of aluminum alloy, with the tensile strength of steel and a unit weight one-third that of steel, could be three times as long: it could hang for 15-3/4 miles. Because it would be three times as long and, moreover, because aluminum stretches under tension three times as much (see Section 3.2), the aluminum cable would stretch nine times as much as the steel cable.

Elongation is not the only deformation accompanying simple tension. Careful measures of the cable before and after the application of the load show that as the load **increases,** and the cable elongates, its diameter **decreases.** This lateral change in dimension was first discovered by the French physicist Poisson at the beginning of the nineteenth century. The ratio of the lateral to the longitudinal strain is called **Poisson's ratio:** it is about one-third for steel. The reduction in diameter of the hanging, 300,000-inch steel cable under its own weight due to Poisson's phenomenon is very minute: about one thousandth of one inch.

5.2 Simple Compression

Compression is the state of stress in which the particles of the material are pushed one against the other [see Fig. 3.7(b)]. A column supporting a weight is under compression: its height shortens under load. Shortening is typical of compression. The shortening of a unit length, or **compressive strain,** is proportional to the load per unit of column area, or **compressive stress.** The ratio of compressive stress to compressive strain is the **elastic modulus** in compression (see Section 3.2).

Deformations in compression are opposite to those in tension: shortening takes place in the direction of the load and lengthening at right angles to it, due to Poisson's phenomenon. Thus, a column of steel capable of carrying its own weight could be made, theoretically, as high as 5-1/4 miles, and would shorten as much as a 5-1/4 mile cable would lengthen.

Structural elements developing simple compression are very common, because, eventually, all loads must be channeled down to earth: they appear in modern steel buildings and in Greek stone temples.

Materials incapable of resisting tension are often strong in compression: stone, masonry, mortar, and concrete can develop high compressive stresses. A column of marble could be built to a height of 10,000 feet before failing in compression, a concrete column could reach a height of 2000 feet. Modern materials with high compressive strength, such as steel, can be used to build columns much slimmer than those of stone or concrete, but their slenderness introduces a new type of limitation in the design of compressive elements.

The reader may be familiar with the early movies of Charlie Chaplin in which he is often seen leaning on a cane, a slim bamboo rod: whenever the little fellow leans heavily on his cane, the cane bends outward (Fig. 5.4). The same behavior is typical of all long, **slender** structural elements under compression. As the compressive load is slowly increased, a value is reached at which the slender element, instead of just shortening, "buckles out," and **usually breaks.** This dangerous value is called the **buckling load** of the element. It becomes a basic design factor whenever the material is strong enough in compression to require only a small cross-sectional area, thus allowing the use of slender elements.

The buckling phenomenon may be usefully visualized from another viewpoint. A slender column shortens when compressed by a weight applied to its top, and, in so doing, lowers the weight's position. The tendency of all weights to lower their position is a basic law of nature. It is another basic law of nature that, whenever there is a choice between different paths, a physical phenomenon will follow the "easiest" path. Confronted with the choice of bending out or shortening, the column finds it easier to shorten for relatively small loads, and to bend out for relatively large loads. In other words, when the load reaches its "buckling" value the column finds it easier to lower the load by bending than by shortening.

82

5.4 Buckling under compression.

It must be realized that, theoretically, the column will bend out even if the load is perfectly centered and the column perfectly homogeneous. In practice, small imperfections in the centering of the load or flaws in the material will facilitate buckling.

The danger of buckling is not related to the stressing of the material above a safe compressive stress, or to its flowing under a state of plastic stress. The value of the compressive load for which a slender column will buckle may produce stresses **below** the safe values determined on the basis of the compressive strength of the material. Buckling is, in a sense, similar to resonance: if an otherwise safe load oscillates in step with the structure, the structure deflects more and more until it fails; if an otherwise safe compressive load is near the buckling load, the column bends out more and more until it breaks.

The buckling load of a column depends on its material, its length, the shape of its cross section, and the restraints applied to its ends. The buckling load is proportional to the elastic modulus of the material: a column of steel is three times stronger against buckling than an identical column of aluminum. The buckling load is inversely proportional to the square of the column length: a column twice as long as another, and with identical cross section has a buckling load four times smaller (Fig. 5.5).

To be strong against buckling and still be efficient, compression members must not be slender and yet must use a limited amount of material. The I-beam, with a thin web and wide flanges, the boxed section, and, in general, cross sections with most of the material away from the center of the section are well suited for this purpose.

The buckling load increases with the restraints at the ends of the compressed member. A cantilevered column buckles as one half of a column twice as long supported at both ends; hence, its buckling load is four times smaller than that for the same simply supported column (Fig. 5.6).

84

5.5 Buckling load versus length.

(a) (b)

(a) (b) (c)

5.6 Influence of restraints on buckling load.

5.3 Simple Shear

Shear is the state of stress in which the particles of the material slide relative to each other [see Fig. 3.7(c)]. Rivets in riveted connections tend to shear (Fig. 5.7). A hole puncher uses shear to punch out holes in a sheet of paper (Fig. 5.8). The weight of a cantilever beam built into a wall tends to shear off the beam from the wall at its "root" (Fig. 5.9).

Shear introduces deformations capable of changing the shape of a rectangular element into a skewed parallelogram (Figs. 5.7, 5.8, 5.9). The **shear strain** is measured by the skew angle of the deformed rectangle (Fig. 5.9) rather than by a change in length, as in the case of tension or compression.

The forces producing this deformation act on the planes along which the sliding takes place, and when measured on one square inch are called **shear stresses** (Fig. 5.10). In the elastic range of behavior the deformation is proportional to the force and, hence, the shear strain is proportional to the shear stress. The ratio of shear stress to shear strain is called the **shear modulus.** It is a characteristic of the material and is about half as large as the elastic modulus in tension or compression: steel, for example, has a shear modulus of 11.5 million pounds per square inch.

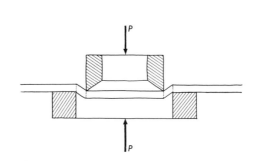

5.7 Shear in rivets.

5.8 Shear punching.

Angle α = shear strain

5.9 Shear strain in beam.

Area = 1 square inch

S = shear stress

5.10 Shear stress.

One of the essential characteristics of shear is to produce sliding along not one but **two planes,** which are always **at right angles** to each other. If a rectangular element is isolated from the root of a cantilevered beam it is seen that, due to the action of the beam weight, vertical shearing forces act on its vertical sides (Fig. 5.11). These forces also have a tendency to rotate the rectangle, just as the pull and push of the driver's arms tend to rotate the steering wheel of a car. If the isolated element is to be in equilibrium in rotation (see Section 4.2), as it is in the actual beam, two equal and opposite forces must act on the horizontal sides of the rectangle to counteract the rotating action of the vertical forces (Fig. 5.12). The horizontal forces required by equilibrium produce a shearing tendency in horizontal planes. Thus, shearing in vertical planes **necessarily** involves shearing in horizontal planes, **and vice versa.**

The existence of the horizontal shearing forces may also be inferred by analyzing the deformation of the rectangular element. The skewing of the element produces a lengthening of one of its diagonals and a shortening of the other. Since lengthening is always accompanied by tension and shortening by compression, the same deformation could be obtained by compressing the element along the shortened diagonal and tensioning it along the other (Fig. 5.13). Thus, shear may also be considered as a combination of tension and compression at right angles in directions making an angle of 45 degrees with the shear directions.

The consideration of shear as the effect of compression and tension is of great practical importance. A material with low tensile strength cannot be strong in shear, as it will fail in tension in a direction at 45 degrees to the directions of shear. Similarly, a **thin** sheet cannot be strong in shear as it will buckle in the direction of the compressive equivalent stress.

88

5.11 Vertical shears.

5.12 Shears required for equilibrium in rotation.

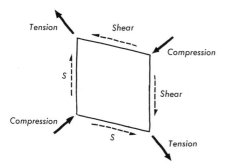

5.13 Equivalence between shear, and tension and compression.

The tendency to slide, characteristic of shear, is found in structural elements twisted by applied loads. Consider a bar of circular cross section, on the surface of which is graphed a square mesh of circles and straight lines [Fig. 5.14(a)]. If this bar is twisted so that one end section rotates in relation to the other, the squares on its surface become skew rectangles [Fig. 5.14(b)]. Since the same kind of deformation can only be due to the same kind of stress, twisting must produce shear strains and, hence, shear stresses in the cross section of the bar and, for equilibrium, also in the radial planes perpendicular to the cross section. This state of stress, although consisting of pure shear, is called **torsion.**

Since torsion develops shear stresses, it must be equivalent to tension and compression at right angles. The housewife who wrings the wet rag before hanging it proves this to be true: the torsion-induced compression squeezes the water out of the rag.

Torsion occurs in a structural element whenever the loads tend to twist it. For example, the eccentric loads transferred by a floor beam to a spandrel beam induce torsional stresses in the spandrel (Fig. 5.15). Rigidity against torsion involves the shear modulus. The most efficient cross sections against torsion are hollow, giving the shear stresses the greatest possible lever arm in rotation around the axis of the bar.

90

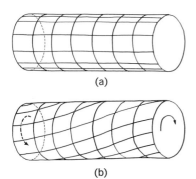

(a)

(b)

5.14 Shear in torsion.

Spandrel

Floor beam

P

5.15 Spandrel beam under torsion.

5.4 Simple Bending

It was stated in Section 5.1 that all complex states of stress are combinations of no more than three basic states of stress: tension, compression, and shear. Compression and tension in different fibers of the same structural element is perhaps the commonest of these combinations: it is called **bending,** and plays an essential role in most structural systems.

Consider a plank supported on two stones with equal lengths cantilevered out (Fig. 5.16). If two boys of equal weight stand at the ends of the plank, the plank ends move downward, while the portion of plank between the stones deflects upward: the curve assumed by the plank between the stones is an arc of a circle.

But the plank has a certain thickness, and **all** of its fibers must become curved: the upper fibers elongate, the lower fibers shorten, and the middle fibers neither elongate nor shorten (Fig. 5.17). Hence, the bending up of the plank induces tension in the upper fibers and compression in the lower fibers. Moreover, the tension and compression increase in proportion to the distance of the fibers from the middle or **neutral** fibers. The state of stress in which the stress varies as a straight line from a maximum tension to a maximum compression is called **simple bending.**

92

5.16 Simple bending.

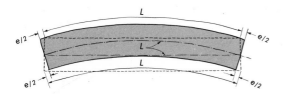

5.17 Strains in bending.

Bending stresses curve along the arc of circle of the deformed plank, but this deformation is so small in comparison with its length that the vertical weights of the two boys may be said to produce practically horizontal stresses. **Bending** may be considered a structural mechanism capable of channeling **vertical** loads in a **horizontal** direction or, more generally, in a direction at right angles to the loads. The weights of the boys are transferred horizontally to the two stones supporting the plank.

In view of the compressive strength of most structural materials, it is relatively easy to channel loads **vertically** down to earth. The fundamental structural problem consists, instead, in transferring vertical loads **horizontally** in order to span the distance between vertical supports. Bending is thus seen to be of prime importance as a structural mechanism.

A good bending material must have practically equal tensile and compressive strength. This explains the predominance of wood among natural structural materials, and the long unrivaled role of steel in modern structures. Reinforced concrete is the only material with bending properties comparable to those of steel. In this man-made material the compressive strength of concrete is used in the compressed fibers of the element, and the tensile strength of steel in the tensioned fibers. If the plank considered above were built of reinforced concrete, it would have reinforcing bars near its top (Fig. 5.18).

94

(a)

(b)

5.18 Reinforced concrete in bending.

Chapter Six

Tension and Compression Structures

6.1 Cables

The high tensile strength of steel, combined with the efficiency of simple tension, makes a steel cable the ideal structural element to span large distances.

Cables are flexible because of their small lateral dimensions in relation to their lengths. Flexibility indicates a limited resistance to bending. Because uneven stresses due to bending are prevented by flexibility, the tensile load is evenly divided among the cable's strands, permitting each strand to be stressed to the same safe, allowable stress.

In order to understand the mechanism by means of which a cable supports vertical loads, one may first consider a cable stretched between two fixed points and carrying a single load at midspan. Under the action of the load the cable assumes a symmetrical, triangular shape, and half the load is carried to each support by simple tension along the two halves of the cable (Fig. 6.1).

The triangular shape acquired by the cable is characterized by the **sag,** the **vertical** distance between the supports and the lowest point in the cable. Without sag the cable could not carry the load, since the tensile forces in it would be horizontal, and no horizontal force can balance a vertical load. At the supports, the inclined pull of the sagging cable may be split into two components: a vertical force equal to half the load, and a horizontal inward pull, or **thrust** (Fig. 6.2). If the supports were not fixed against horizontal displacements, they would move under the action of the thrust, and the two halves of cable would become vertical.

98

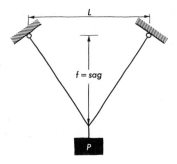

6.1 Symmetrical load on cable.

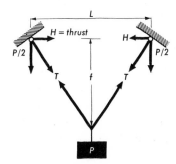

6.2 Cable thrust.

Holding in his hands the ends of a string with a weight attached at its middle, the reader may sense physically that the string develops no thrust when his hands are joined, while an increasing thrust is developed as he moves his hands apart, thus decreasing the string sag. If he chooses a string weak enough, there comes a point where the string snaps, indicating that, as the sag diminishes, the tension eventually becomes larger than the tensile strength of the string. The tensile stress in the cable may be shown to be inversely proportional to the sag: halving the sag doubles the tension in the cable and, consequently, doubles the thrust at the supports (Fig. 6.3).

The cable problem just considered raises an interesting question of economy. A larger sag increases the cable length, but reduces the tensile force in the cable and, hence, allows a reduction of its cross section; a smaller sag reduces the cable length, but requires a larger cross section because of the higher tension developed in the cable (Fig. 6.3). Hence the total volume of the cable, the product of its cross section and its length, is large for both very small and very large sags,. and must be minimum for some intermediate value of the sag. The optimal or "most economical sag" for a given horizontal distance between the supports equals half the span and corresponds to a symmetrical, 45-degree-triangle cable configuration with a thrust equal to half the load (Fig. 6.4).

100

(a)

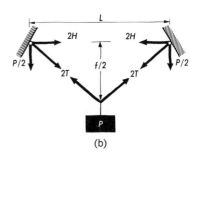

(b)

6.3 Variation of cable reactions with sag.

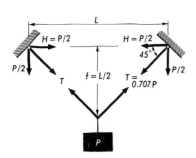

6.4 Optimal sag.

If the **load is shifted** from its midspan position, the **cable changes shape,** and adapts itself to carrying the load by means of straight sides with different inclinations [Fig. 6.5(a)]. The two supports develop different vertical re- actions, but the same thrust, since the cable must be in equilibrium in the horizontal direction. The value of the thrust differs from the value for a centered load, but still varies inversely as the sag. The reader may sense this by shifting the load along the hand-supported string.

If two identical loads are set on the cable in symmetrical locations, the cable again adapts itself, and carries the loads by acquiring a new configuration, with three straight sides [Fig. 6.5(b)]. If the number of loads is increased, the cable acquires new equilibrium configurations with straight sides between the loads, and changes in direction at the points of application of the loads. The shape acquired by a cable under concentrated loads is called **funicular polygon** [Fig. 6.5(c)] (from the Latin word **funis** for rope, and the Greek word **gonia** for angle): it is the **natural** shape required to carry loads in **tension.**

As the number of loads on the cable increases, the funicular polygon acquires an increasing number of smaller sides, and approaches a smooth curve. If one could apply to the cable an infinite number of infinitesimally small loads the polygon would become a **funicular curve.** For example, the funicular

102

6.5 Funicular polygons.

(a) (b) (c)

polygon for a large set of equal loads evenly spaced **horizontally** approaches a well-known geometrical curve, the **parabola** [Fig. 6.6(a)]. The optimal sag for a parabolic cable equals three-tenths of the cable span.

If the equal loads are distributed evenly **along the length** of the cable, rather than horizontally, the funicular curve differs from a parabola, although it has the same general configuration: it is a **catenary,** the natural shape acquired by a cable of constant cross section under its own weight, which is uniformly distributed along its length [Fig. 6.6(b)]. The optimal sag for the catenary is about one-third of the span; for such sag ratio the catenary and the parabola are very similar curves [Fig. 6.6(c)].

A cable carrying its own weight (the dead load) and a load uniformly distributed horizontally, acquires a shape that is intermediate between a catenary and a parabola. This is the shape of the cables in the central span of a suspension bridge, which carry themselves and the stiffening truss on which the roadway is laid (Fig. 6.7).

A cable will span the **largest** possible distance if it can just carry its weight, but will break under the smallest additional load. Assuming an optimal sag-span ratio of one-third, to minimize the weight of the cable, it is found that a steel cable with a strength of 200,000 pounds per square inch could span a distance of 17 miles! This maximum distance is independent of the cable diameter, since both the weight of the cable and its tensile strength are proportional to the area of the cross section. The largest suspension bridge in construction to date, the Verrazano-Narrows Bridge in New York, has a middle span of 4260 feet. The largest suspension bridge designed to date, the bridge over the Messina Straits, has a middle span of over 5000 feet. Such spans are rapidly approaching limiting values, beyond which it is not practically conceivable to go with the types of steel available today. Only an improvement in cable strength will make substantially larger spans possible.

104

(a)

(b)

(c)

6.6 Funicular curves.

6.7 Suspension bridge.

One may wonder why the efficiency and economy of steel cables does not make them more frequently used in smaller structures. The limitations in the application of cables stem directly from their adaptability to changing loads: cables are unstable, and stability is one of the basic requirements of structural systems. The trusses hanging from the cables of a suspension bridge have the purpose not only of supporting the roadway but also of stiffening the cables against motions due to changing or moving loads.

Stiffening trusses are usually rigid in the direction of the bridge axis, but less so in a transverse direction: this explains the fairly large displacements of suspension bridges caused by lateral winds. Moreover, the long roadway and the shallow trusses constitute a thin ribbon, so flexible in the vertical direction that it may develop a tendency to twist and oscillate vertically under steady winds (see Section 2.6). The failure of the Tacoma Bridge in Tacoma, Washington, was due to such aerodynamic oscillations (see Fig. 2.15). Modern suspension bridges are made safe against such dangers by the introduction of stiffening guy wires and by an increase in the bending and twisting rigidity of their roadway cross section.

A cable is not a self-supporting structure unless ways and means are found to absorb its thrust, which in large spans may reach values of the order of millions of pounds. In suspension-bridge design this result is achieved by channeling the tension of the main-span cable over the towers to the cables of the side spans, and by anchoring these cables in the ground. The anchoring blocks of heavy reinforced concrete are usually poured into rock, and resist the thrust both by the action of their own weight and by the reaction of the adjoining rock (Fig. 6.8). Compression in the towers, bending in the trusses, and shear in the anchoring blocks are essential to the stability and strength of the tensile cables of suspension bridges.

More complex cable structures and other tensile structures are considered in Section 6.4.

106

6.8 Anchorage of suspension bridge cables.

6.2 Trusses

A flexible cable supporting a load at midspan was found to be a pure tensile structure. Consider now the structure obtained by flipping the cable up and stiffening its straight sides to make them capable of resisting compression. The "negative sag" or **rise** changes the direction of all the stresses, and the upped cable becomes a pure compressive structure: it is the simplest example of a **truss** (Fig. 6.9).

The load at the top of the truss is channeled by the compressed struts to the supports, which are acted upon by vertical forces equal to half the load, and by **outward** thrusts (Fig. 6.9). The thrust can be absorbed by buttresses of a compressive material, such as masonry, or by a tensile element, such as a steel **tie-rod** (see Fig. 3.9). Such elementary trusses, of wood with iron tie-rods, were built in the Middle Ages to support the roofs of small homes and churches, and there is reason to believe that the Greek temples were covered by wooden structures of similar design. As spans became larger, it was found practical to hang the tie-rod from the top of the truss in order to eliminate the large sag of this relatively flexible element (see Fig. 3.9). A similar triangular element may be built with a "positive sag," using steel rods for the tensile bars and wood for the compressive "tie-rod" (Fig. 6.10).

(a)

(b)

6.9 Triangular truss.

6.10 Truss with compressive strut.

Trusses capable of spanning large distances by means of tension and compression elements only are obtained by combining triangular elementary trusses. For example, a triangulated truss with the bars of the **upper chord** and the **verticals** in compression, and the bars of the **lower chord** and the **diagonals** in tension is shown in Fig. 6.11. The middle load W_1 is channeled along the tension diagonals to the upper points A and B. (The vertical OO' does not carry load, because the horizontal forces of bars O'A and O'B could not equilibrate it.) The compressive upper tie-rod AB absorbs the thrust, while the compressed verticals AC and BD transfer the vertical reactions equal to half W_1 down to the points C and D. The tension diagonal CE channels the reaction and the additional load W_2 to E, and introduces tension in the lower chord member CO. The compression tie-rod EA absorbs the thrust, and the compressed vertical EG transfers the vertical reaction to G. This channeling mechanism occurs in all other **panels** of the truss until the last compressed verticals, IL and MN, carry the total weight of the truss to the supports L and N. If the truss loads were applied only **at** the **panel points** O, C, D, etc., all the truss members would be either tensed or compressed. Since the loads are often applied **between** the panel points, the lower chord bars develop some bending also.

It is sufficient to reverse the inclination of the diagonals to have these bars work in compression, and the verticals in tension. Thus, in Fig. 6.12 the load W_1 is transferred up by the tensioned vertical from O to O', and down the compression diagonals from O' to C and D. CD is a tension tie-rod. The triangular truss CO'D rests on the adjoining panels at C and D; here the additional loads W_2 and W_3 are picked up, transferred to A and B by the tension verticals, and down the compression diagonals to G and H. CG and DH are again tension tie-rods. The channeling of the loads may be continued until the last compression diagonals carry the load to the supports. In this truss the verticals IL, MN, and the last upper chord bars are unnecessary. Similarly, the end verticals and the last lower chord bars would have been unnecessary if the truss of Fig. 6.11 had been supported at I and M. The first scheme is commonly used in highway bridges, the second in railroad bridges, where the truss is often below the roadway.

110

6.11 Triangulated truss with tensed diagonals.

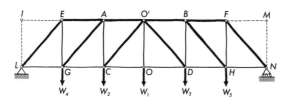

6.12 Triangulated truss with compressed diagonals.

(a) (b)

6.13 Load channeling of trusses.

Upper chord members, verticals, and diagonals may buckle under compression, unless properly designed. One of the first studies on the buckling of bridge structures was prompted at the end of the nineteenth century by the failure in buckling of a Russian railroad bridge. Since, moreover, moving loads may produce either tension or compression in a given member, depending on their location, some trusses are built with both tension and compression diagonals, so that loads may be always carried by both mechanisms.

The combinations of tension and compression bars capable of producing a practical truss are extremely varied. The reader may wish to follow the channeling mechanism in the elementary examples given in Figs. 6.13(a) and 6.13(b), and thus visualize how such structures work.

The bars of a truss are joined by being riveted, bolted, or welded to a "gusset plate" at their intersection (Fig. 6.14). In either case the restraint against relative rotation produced by the gusset plates transforms the truss bars from pure tension or compression members into elements developing a minor amount of additional bending and shear stresses. These so-called **secondary stresses** are considered in Section 7.4.

112

6.14 Gusset plate.

6.15 Composite truss bridge.

6.16 Truss with curved top chord.

Trusses are used to span hundreds of feet between supports. They may be cantilevered from piers and in turn carry other simply supported trusses (Fig. 6.15). Trusses with curved top chords behave very much like suspension bridges (Fig. 6.16). Parallel trusses are commonly used in steel design to cover large halls (Fig. 6.17). Light trusses, called **open web joists,** are used to span small distances, either as roof or as floor structures (Fig. 6.18). Although not as popular today as they were in the nineteen-hundreds, at the beginning of the structural steel era, trusses are to this day one of the essential components of large structures.

114

6.17 Parallel-chord truss roof.

6.18 Open web joist.

6.3 Funicular Arches

The parabolic shape assumed by a cable carrying loads uniformly distributed horizontally may be turned up to give the ideal shape of an arch developing only compression under this type of load (Fig. 6.19). The arch is an essentially compressive structure used to span large distances, and developed by the Romans, the greatest road builders of antiquity. The arch, in a variety of shapes, is also used to span small distances, and may be considered one of the basic structural elements of all types of architecture.

The ideal shape of an arch capable of supporting given loads by means of simple compression may always be found as the shape of the overturned corresponding funicular polygon. It is by this method that the Spanish architect Gaudí determined the form of the arches in the Church of the Sacred Family in Barcelona. The funicular polygon for a set of equal and equally spaced loads **converging towards a common point** is symmetrical about this point (Fig. 6.20). At the limit, when the loads become infinite in number and infinitesimally small, the funicular polygon becomes the funicular curve for a **radial pressure** or **tension,** and is an **arc of a circle.** Hence, the circle cannot be the funicular curve for a vertical load, uniformly distributed either along the horizontal or along the circular arch, since arches can obviously be funicular for only one set of loads.

The shape of a masonry arch is usually chosen to be the funicular of the dead load. But whenever an arch is used in a bridge, a variety of moving loads must be assumed to travel over the arch, and a state of stress other than compression may develop. A cable can carry **any** set of loads in tension by changing shape; an arch cannot change shape and, hence, cannot be funicular for all the loads it is supposed to carry. The stability of the arch implies lack of adaptability. The relative importance of bending stresses in arches is considered in Section 8.4.

116

6.19 Funicular arch.

6.20 Funicular polygon for radial loads.

The channeling of vertical loads along a curve by means of simple compression is today such an elementary concept that it is hard to realize how slow its evolution has been. Practically unknown to the Greeks, it produced the daring and lovely lines of a modern bridge only a few decades ago. The ultimate consequences of the use of **curved** structural elements are even more recent and interesting: they are considered in Chapter 12.

6.4 Cable Roofs

The exceptional efficiency of steel cables suggests their use in the construction of large roofs. This relatively recent development has brought about a number of ingenious solutions, in which tensile cables are the essential element in an otherwise complex structural system.

The simplest cable roof consists of a series of cables hanging from the tops of columns capable of bending resistance, or passing over the tops of compressive struts and anchored to the ground. Straight beams or plates connect the parallel cables, thus creating a polygonal or inverted barrel roof surface (Fig. 6.21). The simplicity and low cost of this scheme would make it popular but for the fact that the straight elements connecting the cables are usually light and tend to oscillate or "flutter" under the action of the wind. To avoid flutter, the roofing material must be relatively heavy, or the cables must be stabilized by guy wires or stiffening trusses.

The suspension-bridge principle has been adopted in a structure designed by Nervi and Covre for a manufacturing plant (Fig. 6.22). The reinforced concrete towers of each roof section (100 feet wide and 830 feet long) are inclined posts supported by shorter compression struts. The horizontal roof consists of reinforced concrete beams and slabs, prefabricated on the ground, and is suspended from the cables by means of wire hangers. This structure permits

118

6.21 Cylindrical cable roof.

6.22 Suspension-bridge roof.

the economic roofing of areas of 10,000 square feet without intermediate columns. The peripheral walls are independent of the roof structure, and must be supported by vertical columns capable of resisting the wind pressure. The relatively heavy horizontal concrete roof acts as stiffening truss and, moreover, stabilizes the cables by its own weight.

A similar principle was used by Saarinen in the Yale University skating rink (Fig. 6.23). The cables are suspended from a central arch, with inverted curvature at the ends, and are anchored to the heavy, peripheral, curved walls of the rink. The roofing material is wood: its relatively light weight does not stabilize the cables entirely.

The solution suggested by Nowicki for the roof of the Raleigh, North Carolina, arena consisted of two inclined intersecting arches of concrete, supported by series of main cables (Fig. 6.24). Cables at right angles to the main cables formed a mesh on which a tent roof could slide. In its present form, the roof consists of lightweight corrugated metal plates, permanently anchored to the cable mesh. The arches are essentially supported by vertical columns, and resist in compression the thrust of the main cables. The surface defined by the cables resembles a saddle, and is more stable under wind loads than a barrel-shaped roof. Notwithstanding the shape of the roof, the lightweight corrugated plates were stabilized by guy wires connecting a number of mesh points to the vertical columns, to avoid flutter.

The same type of saddle roof may be obtained by hanging the cables from a ring curved in space, which acts as compression ring and replaces essentially the two upper portions of the arches in the Nowicki scheme. Such a roof has been proposed but not used by Stubbins to cover a large hall in Berlin, Germany (Fig. 6.25).

120

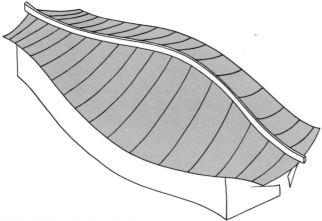

6.23 Cable roof with arch rib.

6.24 Cable roof with saddle shape.

6.25 Cable roof hanging from skew ring.

It was remarked in the preceding section that the circle is the funicular curve for a compression arch acted upon by radial forces. A notable example of a structure built by means of radial tensile elements and a tensile and a compressive ring is the bicycle wheel. The spokes are tensed between the tensed circular hub and the compressed circular rim, forming a structure with high "locked-in" stresses, which is stable against both radial and transverse loads. The roof of the auditorium in Utica, New York, designed by Zetlin, is based on the bicycle-wheel principle (Fig. 6.26). Two series of cables connect the outer compression ring to the upper and lower rims of a central hub, consisting of two separate tension rings connected by a truss system. The cables are kept separate and tensed by compression struts of adjustable length. Each pair of cables can be correctly tensed by turning the turnbuckles of the struts, and the roof, covered by a series of prefabricated metal plates, is practically free of flutter because the high tension in the cables makes them more rigid than if they were free-hanging.

The roof designed by Viera for a stadium in Montevideo, Uruguay, does away with the two series of cables, typical of the bicycle wheel, and is a relatively inexpensive system well suited to roof large circular areas (Fig. 6.27). A single series of cables connects a central tension ring of steel to an outer compression ring of concrete, supported by the cylindrical exterior wall of the stadium. The decking consists of a large number of prefabricated, wedge-shaped concrete slabs, which are supported on the radial cables by the hooked ends of their own reinforcing bars. To reduce instability, each plate is first loaded with bricks or sandbags, temporarily over-tensing the cables, and the radial and circumferential gaps are filled with cement mortar. Once the mortar sets, the entire roof becomes a monolithic concrete "dish." As the overload is then taken off the slabs, the cables tend to shorten, but are prevented from doing so by the monolithic concrete roof in which they are embedded. The inverted roof is thus stiffened by the prestressing of the cables, and shows little tendency to flutter. Similar roofs have been successfully built in the United States.

122

6.26 Bicycle-wheel roof.

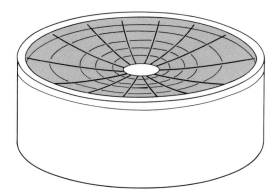

6.27 Prestressed cable roof.

The concept of stiffening the cables against flutter by additional tension, obtained in the case of the Viera roof by overloads, obviously may be extended. For example, one series of cables may be overstressed by tensioning another series of cables at right angles to it.

In the design of airplane hangars it is essential to provide large front doors, which must slide open smoothly. These sliding doors cannot be supported by columns and are usually hung from a top beam, as wide as the hangar. The structural problem to be solved for this type of building consists in covering a rectangular area having columns on not more than three of its sides. A solution, realized by Ammann and Whitney, uses a scheme in which a cantilevered span is equivalent to one half of a suspension bridge (Fig. 6.28). The space between "tower" and "anchorage" is used for offices or shops, while the cable-supported cantilevered roof consists of "folded-plate" reinforced concrete construction (see Section 10.7). The limited weight and high resistance to bending and compression of folded plates, together with the tensile strength of cables, make such structures capable of economically cantilevering as much as 125 feet.

A similar solution has been adopted by Tippets-Abbet-McCarthy and Stratton in roofing the Pan-American arrival building at Idlewild. In this case the roof consists of reinforced-concrete plates supported by radial beams, an outer elliptical ring, and an inner elliptical ring (Fig. 6.29). The beams are cantilevered from the outer ring, and supported by cables going over compression supports at the outer ring, and anchored at the inner ring. The outer ring is supported by compression columns; the inner ring is anchored to tension struts attached to heavy concrete blocks in the ground. The cantilevers, 150 feet long, permit the sheltering of the planes during the embarkation and debarkation of the passengers.

The solutions mentioned above are just a few of the most recently adopted to roof large structures. Whereas the largest span covered by a compressive roof, to date, is 700 feet (in the C.N.F. concrete shell in Paris), tensile roofs can easily span over one thousand feet. In view of the exceptional potentialities of cable roofs it is to be expected that their use will increase with the increasing dimensions of the areas to be covered.

124

6.28 Cable-suspended cantilever roof.

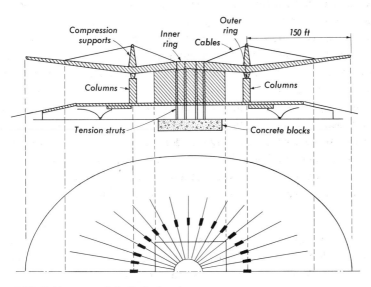

6.29 Cable-suspended elliptical roof.

6.5 Space Frames

When a roof is supported by a number of parallel trusses, the load distributed over the roof is first carried by a transverse system of beams and slabs to the trusses and then by these to the supports (Fig. 6.17). If the covered area is rectangular, the total load is supported by the columns or walls along two parallel sides of the rectangle, while the other two sides are free of supporting elements. Moreover, any load concentrated in the vicinity of a truss is almost entirely carried by this truss, since the transverse elements are too flexible to carry the adjoining trusses down with them. One may thus say that the load-carrying action of each truss occurs essentially in its own plane.

More integral and more efficient behavior of a trussed roof may be obtained by connecting the parallel trusses, not by flexible elements, but by transverse trusses as rigid as the main trusses (Fig. 6.30). In this case, the deflection of a truss is transmitted to the adjoining trusses, and the entire roof works more or less monolithically. Although it is convenient to think of this combination as main trusses connected by transverse trusses, it is in fact difficult to separate the two systems of perpendicular trusses, since some bars of the roof structure are common to trusses of both systems, as bars AB and CD in Fig. 6.31. Such spatial systems of hinged bars are called **space frames,** and offer an economical solution to the roofing of large rectangular areas. Space frames are usually divided into categories depending on the shape of the basic element used to create them. Thus, in Fig. 6.30 the element is rectangular, in Fig. 6.31 triangular. In the first case a combination of Vierendeel trusses at right angles to each other is obtained if the diagonals are omitted (see Section 8.3).

Space frames are stiffer than systems of parallel trusses, and may be made shallower: while the depth of a truss with horizontal upper and lower chords is of the order of one-tenth the span, space frames may have depth as small as one-twentieth or one-thirtieth of the span.

126

6.30 Rectangular space frame.

6.31 Triangulated space frame.

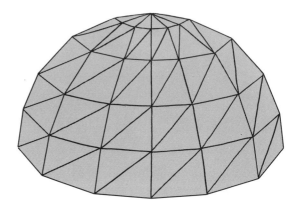

6.32 Schwedler dome.

When the area to be covered is circular and the roof has the shape of a dome, one may subdivide the dome surface into a number of triangles or other regular polygons the sides of which are hinged bars. One of the classical schemes based on this principle is the Schwedler dome illustrated in Fig. 6.32. Figure 6.33 illustrates the Zeiss-Dywidag dome. One of the modern developments of this type of roof is the "geodesic" dome of Buckminster Fuller, in which the triangle and the pentagon are used to obtain a subdivision in terms of bars of equal lengths (Fig. 6.34). Space-frame domes are exceptionally light structures, which permit the spanning of large distances with relative reduction in materials. In this type of structure the connections between the bars are delicate elements and weigh heavily in construction costs.

Radial trusses connected by polygonal rings at various heights are also used to support roofs over circular or polygonal areas (Fig. 6.35). The tension rings absorb the thrust developed at their levels and allow the omission of some of the tension bars in the trusses, thus partially freeing the interior space from disturbing horizontal or inclined elements.

128

6.33 Zeiss-Dywidag dome.

6.34 Geodesic dome.

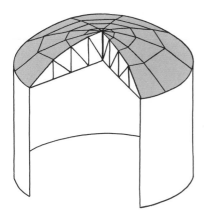

6.35 Radial-truss roof.

Chapter Seven

Beams

7.1 Cantilevered Beams

Beams are among the most commonly used structural elements. Since a majority of loads are vertical and a majority of usable surfaces horizontal, beams are extensively used to transfer vertical loads horizontally. Their mechanism involves a combination of bending and shear. **Cantilevered beams** will be considered first.

By experimenting with a thin steel ruler clamped between his fingers, the reader may verify the following facts:

(a) The deflection of the loaded tip of the cantilevered ruler increases rapidly with the cantilevered length; doubling the length increases the deflection by a factor of eight, which is the **cube** of the lengths ratio (Fig. 7.1).

(b) The deflections are much larger when the width of the ruler is kept horizontal than when the thickness is kept horizontal. Accurate measurements show that the deflections are inversely proportional to the horizontal side of the ruler's cross section, and to the **cube** of its vertical side. If the ruler has sides in the ratio of one to two, in the first case the deflections are inversely proportional to 2 times 1 cubed, in the second to 1 times 2 cubed: the deflections would be four times smaller in the second case than in the first (Fig. 7.2).

(c) The deflections under the same load of two identical rulers made of different materials, such as steel and aluminum, are inversely proportional to the elastic moduli of the materials. The aluminum ruler deflects three times as much as the steel ruler (Fig. 7.3).

(d) Finally, the tip deflection of the cantilevered ruler increases as the load moves from the root towards the tip of the cantilever (Fig. 7.4).

(a)   (b)

7.1 Influence of length on cantilever deflection.

(a)   (b)

7.2 Influence of depth and width on cantilever deflection.

Steel
Modulus of elasticity =
30 million lb/sq in.

Aluminum
Modulus of elasticity =
10 million lb/sq in.

(a)   (b)

7.3 Influence of material on cantilever deflection.

(a)   (b)

7.4 Influence of load location on cantilever deflection.

Another geometrical factor determines deflection and merits detailed consideration: the shape of the cross section. We shall first consider a beam of rectangular cross section.

The deflection of the loaded tip of the cantilever is due to the deformation of the originally straight beam into a slightly curved element. Such deformation requires the elongation of the upper fibers and the shortening of the lower fibers of the beam, and produces the state of stress defined in Section 5.4 as **bending.** Bending stresses vary linearly from a maximum tensile value at the top fiber to a maximum compressive value at the bottom fiber, and vanish at the middle fiber, the so-called **neutral axis** of the beam (Fig. 7.5). The load, through its lever arm, tends to rotate the beam downward; the bending stresses, through their lever arm (which equals two-thirds of the beam depth), tend to rotate the beam upward, and establish equilibrium in rotation. The deeper the beam, the larger the lever arm of the bending stresses; hence, for the same value of the allowable stress at the top and bottom fibers, the deeper beam is capable of equilibrating a larger load. Since stresses are constant across the width of the beam, an increase in depth is more profitable than an increase in width: how profitable, is shown by the decrease in deflection with the **cube** of the depth (Fig. 7.2).

134

7.5 Bending of cantilever beam.

The behavior described above is typical of beams with a length at least **twice** their depth. **Deep beams**—that is, beams with a length less than twice their depth—support the load mostly by shear and do not exhibit a linear variation of stress across their depth.

A beam of rectangular cross section is obviously inefficient in bending, since most of its fibers are not stressed up to the allowable stress; in fact, only its top and bottom fibers reach the allowable stress, while all other fibers are unavoidably understressed. This inefficiency can be remedied by re-locating most of the beam material near the top and bottom of the beam. The cross section of an I-beam, with most of the material in **flanges** connected by a thin **web,** has these characteristics (Fig. 7.6). The large area of the flanges develops stresses up to the allowable limit with a lever arm equal to the depth of the beam, and contributes substantially to the bending action. The smaller web area is near the neutral axis and contributes negligibly to bending. If **all** the material of a beam of rectangular cross section could be shifted towards its top and bottom, creating an "ideal I-section" without web, its rigidity would increase by a factor of three. This means that deflections and stresses would decrease by a factor of three, or, to put it the other way around, that the beam could support three times as much load with the same allowable stress (Fig. 7.7).

Splitting the web of an I-beam in two and shifting the material laterally produces another cross section just as efficient in bending and more efficient in torsion, the "box section" (Fig. 7.8). The symmetrical I-section and the box section are typical of materials with equal strength in tension and compression;

136

7.6 I-beam cross section.

Rectangular beam

Ideal I-beam

7.7 Variation of strength with cross-section shape.

7.8 Box section.

different shapes become more logical when these strengths differ. For example, the compressive strength of concrete is approximately one-twentieth of the tensile strength of steel; hence, in a reinforced-concrete beam the area of concrete must be much larger than the area of steel. This leads to a T-section, in which the horizontal flange is made of concrete, and the steel is concentrated in the web (Fig. 7.9). In the case of cantilevered beams, the T-beam is inverted: the flange is at the bottom and the web at the top, since the compressed fibers are at the bottom of the beam. The reinforced-concrete T-beam acts very much like an I-beam in which the area of one of the flanges is shrunk because its material is stronger, but T-beams of steel are also used, mainly to facilitate connections with other beams (Fig. 7.10).

The bending stiffness of a cross-sectional shape is gauged by a quantity called its **moment of inertia.** The moment of inertia is proportional to the area of the cross section, i.e., to the amount of material used, but also, and more significantly, to the square of a length that measures the moving of the material away from the neutral axis. The deflections and bending stresses in a beam are inversely proportional to the moment of inertia of its cross section. Moments of inertia for various types of cross section appear in standard beam tables, so that the designer can gauge the strength and rigidity of a given beam without lengthy calculations.

The bending stresses and deflections of a cantilever depend on the location of the loads. The greater the lever arm of the load, the greater the bending stresses (tension, compression) it produces, since for equilibrium in rotation (see Section 4.2) the tension or compression force multiplied by its lever arm must equal the load multiplied by its lever arm (Fig. 7.5). Consequently, the largest stresses occur at the root of the cantilever, the point farthest from the load. For example, if the same total load is first applied at the tip of the cantilever and then evenly distributed over the beam, the bending stresses reduce in the ratio of two to one and the deflections in the ratio of eight to three (Fig. 7.11).

138

7.9 Reinforced-concrete T-section.

7.10 T-beam connection.

$pL = P$

7.11 Deflections due to concentrated and distributed load.

The influence of the lever arm of the load on the stresses introduces another type of inefficiency in the bending mechanism of beams, even when I-sections are used. The I-section was seen to stress most of the beam material up to the allowable values. But this can occur only at the **most stressed** beam section, i.e., at the root; elsewhere the stresses are bound to be smaller because the lever arm of the load is smaller. Maximum stresses are developed only in the small portion of the beam near its root, while everywhere else the beam is understressed. Efficiency may be restored somewhat by varying the cross section of the beam from its tip to its root. Although this is not practical for small cantilevers, it becomes mandatory for large ones. The change in section may be obtained either by increasing the area of the flanges from tip to root, while maintaining the beam depth constant, or by maintaining the area of the flanges constant but increasing the beam depth, or by increasing both the flange area and the beam depth (Fig. 7.12). Thus, as the lever arm of the load increases, either the tensile and compressive **forces** in the flanges or else their lever arm also increases, keeping the beam in equilibrium without a substantial increase in **stress.** The sloping bottom of cantilever beams is the visual evidence of the increased lever arm of beam forces necessary to counterbalance the increasing lever arm of the loads.

Whenever depth limitations permit, it is economical to set the flanges of an I-beam as far apart as possible, thus reducing their area to a minimum, but it must be also remembered that **any** thin compressed element has a tendency to buckle (see Section 5.2). If the compression flange or the web of an I-beam is thin, it may buckle. The web buckles when its compressed fibers, located below the neutral axis, bend out of the vertical plane. The compression flange buckles by bending out in its own horizontal plane, since the web prevents its otherwise easier buckling in a vertical plane. In either case the cross section of the beam rotates and the beam twists (Fig. 7.13). Such buckling of an entire cross section, due to the buckling in compression of some of its fibers, does actually take place during construction when very long I-beams are gripped at midspan and lifted, so that each half of the beam acts as a cantilever. In order to prevent this bending-and-twisting buckling, usually called **lateral buckling,** the beam cross section must be sufficiently strong in bending and torsion (see Section 5.3).

140

7.12 Tapered cantilever beam.

7.13 Lateral buckling.

So far only the bending effects of the tip load have been considered. As pointed out in Section 5.3, the load also tends to shear the beam at the point where it is clamped into the supporting wall. Actually the tendency to shear occurs everywhere in the beam, and is independent of the beam length: if the beam were clamped nearer its tip, the load would have the same tendency to shear it there (Fig. 7.14).

The presence of vertical shear in the beam becomes evident if one notices that a vertically sliced beam is unable to carry vertical loads, but that its carrying capacity is restored if the vertical slices are sewed together by horizontal wires, so as to prevent their relative sliding. The reader may perform an experiment of the same nature by trying to lift a row of books: he will not be able to do so, unless he presses the books together, thus creating between them a large amount of friction which prevents their sliding (Fig. 7.15).

It was shown in Section 5.3 that vertical shear is always accompanied by horizontal shear (see Fig. 5.12). The influence of horizontal shear on the rigidity of a rectangular beam may be visualized by considering the beam "sliced" horizontally into a number of rectangular beams of limited depth. Under the action of a tip load, this assemblage of superimposed beams presents large deflections, because each slice is free to slide with respect to the others, and acts as a shallow, flexible beam (Fig. 7.16). The sliding of the various slices shows the tendency of the beam fibers to shear along horizontal planes. This tendency is prevented by shear stresses along the horizontal planes, obtained either by gluing the various slices together or by sticking vertical pins across the entire depth of the group of slices. When shear is developed, the slices act as a single beam, and the deflections under the same load are considerably reduced. Remembering that the moment of inertia of a

142

(a)   (b)

7.14 Deformations due to shear only.

7.15 Vertical shear in row of books.

(a)   (b)

7.16 Superimposed shallow beams.

rectangular beam is proportional to the cube of its depth, the ratio between the moment of inertia of the monolithic beam and that of four identical slices equals the ratio between one, and four times the cube of one-fourth: the monolithic beam is 16 times more rigid than the separate four slices (Fig. 7.16).

The essential function of the web in the I-section is to develop the shear stresses necessary to have the two flanges work together. Without web, each flange would act as a **separate** shallow beam, and the moment of inertia of the cross section would be small. The flanges connected by the web act monolithically so that the I-section acquires a large moment of inertia. It is thus seen that **the transmission of shear through the web is essential to the bending action of the flanges,** and that shear and bending are interdependent beam actions.

The bending stresses are distributed linearly across the depth of the beam section (Fig. 7.5). The shear stresses may be shown to be distributed parabolically across the depth of a **rectangular** beam, with a maximum value **at** the neutral axis (Fig. 7.17). This maximum is one and a half times the average of the shear stress—that is, one and a half times the load divided by the area of the cross section. In I-beams bending action is essentially provided by the flanges and shear action by the web: the maximum shear stress is approximately equal to the load divided by the area of the web. The shear stresses increase from the tip to the root in proportion to the load, and are also maximum at the root (Fig. 7.18).

7.2 Simply Supported Beams

A beam is said to be **simply supported** when it is supported at both ends, so that its ends are free to rotate, and the beam is free to expand or contract longitudinally (Fig. 7.19).

144

7.17 Shear-stress distribution across rectangular beam depth.

7.18 Shear distribution along cantilever beam.

7.19 Simply supported beam.

A simply supported beam transfers a load applied at midspan half to one support and half to the other. It bends and deflects. Because of symmetry the midspan section moves downward, but remains vertical. Hence, each half of the beam acts as an upside-down cantilever half the length of the beam, loaded by half the load at its tip (Fig. 7.20). Since cantilever deflections are proportional to the tip load and to the cube of the length (see Section 7.1), the deflection of the simply supported beam is one-half of one-eighth, or one-sixteenth that of a cantilever of equal length under the same load. By the same token, the half load acting through a lever arm half the length of the beam produces maximum stresses one-fourth of those in the cantilever. A simply supported beam is stronger and stiffer than a cantilever of the same length: it can carry a load four times as large and will deflect only one-fourth as much under this larger load.

When the same load is evenly distributed over the beam, the stresses in the beam become one-half, and the deflections five-eighths, as large as when the load is concentrated at midspan (Fig. 7.21).

The bending stresses in a uniformly loaded beam are **maximum at midspan,** the point corresponding to the roots of the two half beams considered as upside-down cantilevers. The shearing action is maximum in the neighborhood of the support, where the support reactions tend to move the beam up while the **total** load tends to move it down. The shear **vanishes at midspan,** where there is no tendency for adjoining sections to slide either up or down. The vanishing of the shearing action at the point where bending stresses are greatest is a characteristic of beam behavior for any and all types of simply supported beams.

Nonuniform loads produce similar bending and shearing actions in a simply supported beam. Concentrated loads near the supports have a reduced bending influence, owing to the reduction of their lever arms, but increase the shearing effect. In fact, as a load approaches one of the supports a larger fraction of the load is transferred to this support, while the other is unloaded (Fig. 7.22). When the load is in the immediate neighborhood of a support, the shearing force equals the total load, whereas it was equal to only half the load when the load was at midspan.

146

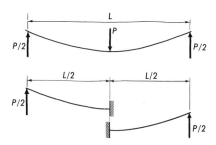

7.20 Concentrated load on simply supported beam.

$$pL = P$$

7.21 Distributed load on simply supported beam.

7.22 Reactions due to unsymmetrical load.

It was noted in Section 5.3 that shear may be considered as a combination of tension and compression at right angles. The presence of maximum shearing effects near the supports of a beam is clearly shown by 45-degree cracks appearing near the supports of reinforced-concrete beams that have inadequate shear reinforcement. Isolating a beam element in this region and applying to it the corresponding shear stresses or the equivalent tensile and compressive stresses at 45 degrees (see Section 5.3), it is seen that the cracks are perpendicular to the direction of the equivalent tensile stress (Fig. 7.23). In order to avoid them, reinforcing bars must be added, running at a 45-degree angle towards the supports and capable of absorbing the tensile stresses due to shear (Fig. 7.24).

The effects of the cross section's shape are the same for simply supported beams as for cantilever beams. Small beams may be built with a uniform cross section; large beams usually have a variable cross section, obtained by increasing the area of the flanges near the center of the beam (where the bending stresses are larger) rather than by increasing the depth of the beam at midspan. **Built-up girders** are beams with variable flange areas, built of angles or plates, and used to carry heavy loads over spans up to a hundred feet or more (Fig. 7.25).

Simply supported beams develop tension in the bottom fibers and compression in the top fibers. The reinforcing bars in a concrete simply supported beam run along its bottom and, if necessary, are increased in numbers or in area towards the center of the beam (Fig. 7.24).

148

7.23 Shear cracks near beam supports.

7.24 Reinforced-concrete simply supported beam.

Stiffeners

7.25 Plate girder.

In steel beams the compressive stresses, particularly high at midspan, may produce buckling of the upper flange and of the upper part of the web, thus causing a twist of the entire cross section. This twisting action may be encouraged by loads not applied directly over the web, but displaced sideways over the upper flange, which by their location have a tendency to twist the beam (Fig. 7.26).

The largest rolled wide-flange section manufactured in the United States is 36 inches deep, weighs 300 pounds per foot, and may carry a load of 6000 pounds per foot, besides its own dead load, over a span of 50 feet. The largest distance such a wide flange beam can span is one for which the beam carries safely its own dead load, but no additional live load. With an allowable bending stress of 30,000 pounds per square inch (20,000 pounds per square inch is the more commonly used value), this maximum span is 271 feet. But the maximum distance can be spanned only if the twisting of the beam in buckling is prevented by the restraint of adjoining structural elements, such as transverse beams or slabs. When the beam is free to twist, the danger of lateral buckling reduces the maximum span to about **one-half** the previous value, or 150 feet. In order to span larger distances the web must be strengthened against buckling in twist by **vertical stiffeners** (Fig. 7.25).

The large amount of material inefficiently used in the neighborhood of the neutral axis of a beam suggests the elimination of some of it by openings, which would also make the beam lighter (Fig. 7.27). As the openings become larger, the beam gradually is transformed into a truss. In a truss, considered as a beam with openings, the upper and lower chords act as the upper and lower flanges of an I-beam, while the diagonals and the verticals absorb the shearing forces, and act as a discontinuous web. By varying the distance

150

7.26 Twist-producing loads.

7.27 I-beam with openings.

between the chords, or by properly distributing the area of the chord members according to the variation of the bending action, and by locating the verticals according to the variation of the shearing effect, trusses can be designed for maximum efficiency (Fig. 7.28).

Beams must be designed for stiffness as much as for strength. It is customary to limit beam deflections to about one three-hundredth of their span in buildings, and one eight-hundredth in bridges. Thus a plate-girder bridge, 200 feet long, should not deflect more than three inches under maximum loads, while a beam 30 feet long is unacceptable if it deflects more than 1.2 inches. When the dead load represents the largest share of loads, beams may be built with a "camber," that is, an upward deflection equal to the downward deflection due to the dead load; the live load then introduces additional deflections contained within acceptable limits.

Combinations of simply supported and cantilevered beams are often used to span long distances. The longest reinforced-concrete bridge in the world, the Maracaibo Bridge in Venezuela, has main spans consisting of beams on three supports with cantilevered portions, and intermediate beams simply supported at the tip of the cantilevers (Fig. 7.29). The outside supports are provided by tension members hanging from high towers. Thus an efficient combination of tensile and bending structures allows the spanning of 1386 feet between towers, while coping with the effects of thermal expansion by the use of a rocker connection between the simply supported spans and the cantilevered spans.

7.3 Fixed Beams and Continuous Beams

It was noted in the previous section that a uniformly loaded, simply supported beam is inefficient, because the bending stresses reach their allowable value only at midspan. The beam fibers curve upwards all along the beam, presenting their greatest curvature at midspan (Fig. 7.30).

152

7.28 Maximum-efficiency truss.

7.29 Combination of simply supported
and cantilevered beams.

7.30 Deflected beam axis.

An obvious way of improving the beam efficiency consists in shifting the supports towards the center of the span, whenever this is feasible. The beam thus acquires two cantilevered portions, and the load on the cantilevers balances in part the load between the supports. The deflection at midspan is reduced and the curvature over the supports is reversed; the beam curves up towards the middle of the span and down towards its ends [Fig. 7.31(c)].

It is interesting to examine the beam behavior as the length of the cantilevers decreases. When both supports are very near the midspan section, the two halves of the beam are cantilevered, and the curvature is down everywhere. The largest stresses occur at the support, and are equal and opposite in value to those developed in the simply supported beam [Fig. 7.31(a)].

When the ratio of cantilevered length to supported span is 1 to 2, the center deflection is practically zero. The largest stresses occur over the supports, and are four times smaller than those in the beam supported at the ends [Fig. 7.31(b)].

When the ratio of cantilever to span lengths is 1 to 2.5 **the sections of the beam over the supports do not rotate;** the stresses over the supports are twice the stresses at midspan, and five times smaller than the stresses in the same beam supported at the ends [Fig. 7.31(c)].

When the ratio of cantilever to span lengths is 1 to 3 the stresses over the supports are **equal** and opposite to those at midspan and six times smaller than in the beam supported at the ends [Fig. 7.31(d)]. This is the **best** distribution of stresses that may be obtained.

When the ends of a beam are built into a **rigid** element and are thus prevented from rotating, the beam behaves as the supported span of a beam with cantilevers in the ratio of 1 to 2.5 [Fig. 7.31(c)]. Such a uniformly loaded, **fixed-**

154

(a)

(b)

(c)

(d)

$-T = $ Compression

7.31 Bottom fiber stress T in beam with cantilevered ends.

end beam has the largest bending stresses at the built-in ends. These stresses are twice as large as the stresses at midspan, and two-thirds as large as the stresses in the same span simply supported. Provided the beam can develop tensile or compressive stresses at top and bottom, it can carry a load **50 per cent higher than an identical simply supported beam,** whenever shear does not govern. Moreover, the fixed beam is **five times stiffer** than the simply supported beam; its midspan deflection is one-fifth that of the simply supported beam. Fixed beams of concrete must have the tensile reinforcement at the bottom near midspan, and at the top near the supports (Fig. 7.32).

The deflected axis of a fixed beam changes from downward to upward curvature at two points, called **inflection points,** where bending stresses vanish, and a stress reversal occurs [Fig. 7.31(c)]. The lack of bending stresses at inflection points indicates that the beam behaves as if it were simply supported at such points, since bending stresses vanish at the ends of a simply supported beam. Thus a beam with fixed ends behaves as a beam simply supported on a **shorter** span with two cantilevered ends, and this explains its greater load capacity and its greater rigidity.

Fixed beams present the added advantage of a greater resistance to buckling when compressed. Whereas in a buckled, simply supported beam the top fibers are entirely compressed, in a fixed beam only about 56 per cent of their length is in compression at the top, and about 44 per cent at the bottom. Remembering that the buckling load is inversely proportional to the square of the compressed length, a compressed fixed beam and, hence, a fixed end column are found to be four times as strong in buckling as a simply supported beam or column (see Section 5.2).

The resistance to **lateral** buckling is inversely proportional to the beam length between inflection points. A fixed beam is only twice as strong against lateral buckling as an identical simply supported beam.

156

7.32 Fixed-end beam of reinforced concrete.

Simply supported and fixed-end beams present the two extreme cases of support conditions. The first allows the unrestrained rotation of the beam ends; the second completely prevents such rotation. In practice, any intermediate condition may prevail. The wall into which the beam is built may not prevent the rotation entirely, or the beam may be **continuous** over more than two supports. In the last case each span, if cut from the others, deflects down and curves up as a simply supported beam [Fig. 7.33(a)]. Continuity with the other spans reverses the curvature over the supports and restrains the rotation of the ends common to two spans [Fig. 7.33(b)]. Depending on the relative lengths and rigidities of the various spans, the rotations are more or less prevented, and each span develops stresses and deflections intermediate between those of simply supported and fixed-end spans.

The continuity of a beam over many supports introduces new characteristics in its behavior. If each span were simply supported and only one span were loaded, the load would be supported exclusively by the bending and shear stresses of the loaded span [Fig. 7.33(c)]. Continuity makes the loaded span stiffer by restraining its end rotations. The entire beam participates in the load-carrying mechanism, and some of the load may be considered as transferred to the unloaded spans [Fig. 7.33(d)].

The stresses due to continuity peter out as one moves away from the loaded span. The curvature in the continuous beam is greatest **under** the load and is "damped out" by the supports, so that stresses become practically negligible two or three spans away from the loaded span [Fig. 7.34(a)]. Continuity increases the resistance of a beam to concentrated loads, but its effect diminishes rapidly, becoming negligible a few supports away from the load.

158

(a)

(b)

(c)

(d)

7.33 Continuous beam.

It may finally be noticed that, depending on the location of the load, the curvature of a given span may change from downward to upward, or vice versa [Fig. 7.34(b)]. Hence, continuous beams of reinforced concrete must have tensile reinforcement at both top and bottom whenever moving loads may be located on different spans, as is the case in bridges.

7.4 Secondary Bending Stresses

Compressive and tensile stresses **constant** through the depth of a structural element are called **direct stresses** to distinguish them from bending stresses, which vary linearly through the depth from a maximum compression to a maximum tension. Direct stresses allow a more efficient use of the material than bending stresses because they develop the same stress in every fiber of the element. The bars of a truss, for example, develop their maximum resistance at all points of their cross sections, since they are acted upon by simple tension or simple compression.

One of the essential characteristics of direct stress is to develop displacements that are extremely small in comparison with bending displacements. The shortening of a ruler by a compressive load cannot be gauged by the naked eye [Fig. 7.35(a)]; but the bending deflection of the tip of the ruler under the same load is quite noticeable [Fig. 7.35(b)]. The bending deflection is often two or three thousand times larger than the compression shortening due to the same load; in other words, a structure is much stiffer in tension or compression than in bending.

Unfortunately, pure compression or tension elements are not easily realizable in practice, as the example of a simple truss will clearly indicate.

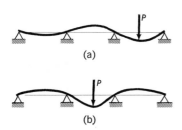

(a)

(b)

7.34 Change of curvature in continuous beam.

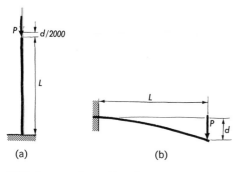

(a)

(b)

7.35 Compressive and bending deflections.

The triangular bracket of Fig. 7.36 is acted upon by a vertical load at its tip; it supports the load as an elementary truss by tension in the inclined bar and compression in the horizontal bar. Direct stresses develop in these bars only if their ends are free to rotate; otherwise the lower bar, for example, would behave as a cantilevered beam and carry part of the load by bending action (Fig. 7.37). Ideally, the bars of a truss should be connected to the supports and to one another by joints allowing unrestrained rotations, or so-called **hinges.**

Some of the truss bridges built in the nineteenth century were actually provided with hinges. But because of weathering, rusting, and painting, the hinges often become locked, and the bars of modern trusses are all riveted or welded in order to avoid prohibitive maintenance costs. In this case, even if the small amount of bending due to the dead load of the bars is neglected, it may easily be seen that additional bending stresses are introduced by the welding or riveting of the bar ends. In the bracket of Fig. 7.36, under the action of the load the upper bar elongates and the lower bar shortens. If the bars were hinged, they would rotate so as to bring the tips of the lengthened and shortened bars together again, and these rotations would change the angle between the bars (Fig. 7.36). Such angle changes are prevented by the rigid welded or riveted connection. In order to maintain the angle unchanged, the bars must bend, and develop bending stresses (Fig. 7.38). These so-called **secondary** bending stresses may reach values as high as 20 per cent of the direct stresses.

The presence of bending stresses can always be detected by visualizing the deformation of a bar. In a continuous beam on four supports, loaded on the middle span only, the deflection shows that the center span develops bending stresses with tension at the bottom and compression at the top, towards midspan, while the outer spans and the portion of the middle span nearer the supports have inverted stresses [Fig. 7.34(b)]. Similarly, in the riveted bracket the bending stresses produce tension in the outer fibers and compression in the inner fibers of both bars, if the ends connected to the wall are hinged (Fig. 7.38). When the connections to the wall are also fixed, the horizontal bar behaves like a beam with fixed ends, and its stresses change from tension to compression at both the outer and the inner fibers (Fig. 7.39).

162

7.36 Truss bracket.

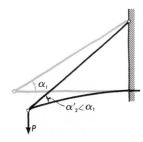

7.37 Bending action in bracket.

7.38 Bending deformations of bracket hinged to wall.

7.39 Bending deformations of bracket fixed to wall.

The visualization of deflections is most useful in determining a state of locked-in stress not caused by loads. Such is the state of stress due to the uneven settlement of the foundations of a building (see Section 2.5). If the right support of a simply supported beam settles more than the left, the beam adapts to this situation by rotating around the hinges and acquiring a slightly tilted position, **without becoming stressed** [Fig. 7.40(a)]. If the beam has fixed ends, the end rotations are prevented, and the beam bends [Fig. 7.40(b)]. Its midspan section presents an inflection point and does not develop bending stresses. The two beam halves behave like two cantilevers carrying a load at their tip [Fig. 7.40(c)].

The advantages of fixed-end beams are balanced by some disadvantages; fixed-end beams are more sensitive to settlements, which may not be easily foreseen. Whenever the danger of foundation settlements is present, a structural system should be chosen capable of adapting to such conditions without straining or stressing.

Considerations of the same kind hold for **differential** deformations due to temperature. The outer columns of a tall building elongate when the temperature of the outside air rises, while the interior columns do not if the building is air-conditioned. The ends of a beam connecting an outer to an inner column acquire different levels, and may develop additional bending stresses (Fig. 7.41). A relative lengthening or shortening of the bars of a truss may occur because of the difference in temperature of the bars. Here again, a structural system capable of adapting itself to deformations by developing minor stresses is superior to a rigid system. Both rigidity and flexibility have their place in structural design, but must be given different weight depending on the loading conditions to be considered.

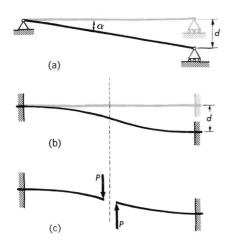

(a)

(b)

(c)

7.40 Uneven settlements of beam ends.

7.41 Thermal deformation of building frame.

Chapter Eight

Frames and Arches

8.1 Post and Lintel

From time immemorial the problem of sheltering human beings from the weather has been solved by an enclosure of walls topped by a roof. In prehistoric times walls and roof were made of stone, without any distinction between the supporting structure and the protecting "skin." A separation of the supporting and protecting functions leads to the simplest "framed" system: the **post and lintel** (Fig. 8.1).

The **lintel** is a beam simply supported on the posts, and carrying the roof load. The **posts** are vertical struts compressed by the lintel. The posts must also resist some horizontal loads, such as the wind pressure; this resistance comes from a bending capacity in the case of wooden or steel posts, from their own weight in stone or masonry piers. Some connection between post and lintel must also be provided, lest the wind blow the roof away.

The foundations of the posts carry the roof and post loads to the ground by means of **footings** which spread the load and guarantee that soil deflections are limited (Fig. 8.1). In any case, the posts and the foundations are essentially under compression, and this is characteristic of the post-and-lintel system.

Post-and-lintel systems may be built one on top of another to frame multistory buildings. In this case the lintels are supported by vertical columns, or walls of stone or masonry as high as the entire building (Fig. 8.2). Construction of this type, while capable of carrying vertical loads, is not well suited to resist horizontal loads, and is easily damaged by hurricane winds and earthquakes, because masonry or stone elements have little bending resistance, and a strong connection between the horizontal and the vertical structural elements is not easily developed.

168

8.1 Post and lintel.

8.2 Multistory post-and-lintel system.

8.2 The Simple Frame

The action of the post-and-lintel system changes substantially if a rigid connection is developed between the lintel and bending-resistant posts. This new structure, the **simple** or **single-bay rigid frame,** behaves monolithically, and is stronger against both vertical and horizontal loads (Fig. 8.3).

Under a uniform load the lintel of a post-and-lintel system deflects, and its ends rotate freely with respect to the posts, which remain vertical. In order to grasp the action of the rigid frame under the same load, one may first consider the horizontal beam as simply supported, and the columns as rigidly connected to the rotated ends of the beam, so as to stick out in a straight, inclined position [Fig. 8.4(a)]. In order to bring back the feet of the columns under the ends of the beam, the columns must be forced inward by horizontal forces, and the ends of the beam must rotate partially backwards. In their final position both the beam and the columns of the frame are curved and develop bending stresses [Fig. 8.4(b)]. The beam has partially restrained ends, and behaves like the center span of a continuous beam on three supports [see Fig. 7.34(b)].

8.3 Simple hinged frame.

8.4 Hinged-frame deflection.

Three consequences of rigidly connecting the horizontal and vertical elements of the frame are immediately apparent: (a) the beam has partially restrained ends, it becomes more rigid, and it is capable of supporting a heavier load in bending (see Section 7.3); (b) the columns are subjected not only to the compressive loads of the roof and of their own weight, but also to bending stresses due to the continuity with the beam; (c) a new **horizontal** force is required to maintain the frame in equilibrium under vertical loads, the **thrust,** which brings back the columns to their vertical position, and introduces compression in the beam. The thrust is typical of frame action. It may be provided by the resistance of the foundation to lateral displacements, that is, by the natural buttressing action of the rock [Fig. 8.5(a)], by buttresses of stone or masonry built for this purpose [Fig. 8.5(b)], or by a tie-rod, which does not permit the frame to open up under the action of vertical loads [Fig. 8.5(c)].

(a)

(b)

(c)

8.5 Thrust absorption.

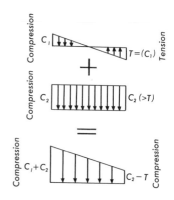

8.6 (a) Stresses due to compression and bending.

All three members of a simple frame are bent **and** compressed. Simple bending develops a linear stress distribution across the depth of the element, with maximum tensile and compressive stresses of equal value; compression adds a constant compressive stress and develops the trapezoidal stress distributions shown in Fig. 8.6. Usually compression prevails in the columns so that their stresses are entirely compressive [Fig. 8.6(a)]; bending prevails in the beam, so that tensile stresses are developed in some parts of the beam [Fig. 8.6(b)].

The foot of the column may be either "hinged" or "fixed." In steel frames the first type of connection may be provided by an actual hinge [Fig. 8.7(a)] or by suitably located anchor bolts; in reinforced-concrete frames it is provided by crossing the reinforcing bars so as to reduce the bending capacity of the section [Fig. 8.7(b)]. The deformation of the frame under vertical load shows that a hinged frame has tensile stresses on the outer column fibers and compressive stresses on the inner fibers [Fig. 8.4(b)].

The deformations of a fixed frame under vertical loads show that the columns develop an inflection point (Fig. 8.8). Since the inflection point is equivalent to a hinge where no bending stresses are developed, the fixed frame is equivalent to a hinged frame with shorter columns. Hence, the fixed frame is stiffer than the hinged frame, and the thrust in the fixed frame is **greater** than in the hinged frame, since it takes a larger force to bring back its shorter, stiffer equivalent columns.

174

8.6 (b) Stresses due to compression and bending.

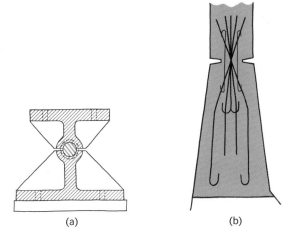

(a)

(b)

8.7 Steel and reinforced-concrete hinges.

8.8 Simple fixed frame.

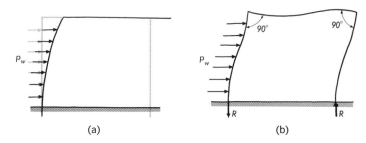

(a)   (b)

8.9 Post-and-lintel and fixed frame under wind load.

Frames are stronger against vertical loads than post-and-lintel systems, but their action is even more advantageous in resisting lateral loads. A post loaded by a horizontal load, such as the wind pressure, acts as a single cantilevered beam without any collaboration from the lintel or the opposite post [Fig. 8.9(a)]. In the frame, instead, continuity with the beam transfers part of the wind load to the opposite column, as shown by the fact that both columns bend [Fig. 8.9(b)]. Even if the beam were hinged at the tops of the columns, it would carry approximately half the wind load to the leeward column, and cut in half the bending stresses in the columns (Fig. 8.10). Since, moreover, the rigidity of the frame corners compels the beam to bend together with the columns, an additional restraint is introduced in the columns, which become more rigid [Fig. 8.9(b)]. Their deflection is reduced, and so are their bending stresses.

The tendency of the frame to turn over due to the pressure of the wind is balanced by additional stresses in the columns: tension in the windward column and compression in the leeward column [Fig. 8.9(b)]; but these stresses are bound to be small because their lever arm is equal to the width of the frame. The lateral displacement or **sidesway** produced in a frame by lateral loads is also present when unsymmetrical vertical loads are applied to the frame (Fig. 8.11).

Whenever the beam of a fixed frame is stronger in bending than the columns, the inflection points in the columns appear approximately at mid-height; the shortened legs of the equivalent hinged frame show that the fixed frame is

176

8.10 Wind load on frame with hinged bar.

8.11 Sidesway under vertical load.

stiffer than the hinged frame against lateral loads also (Fig. 8.12). In either type of frame lateral loads must be considered acting from either side of the frame, so that the reinforcement of concrete frames must be located along both the inner and the outer fibers of the posts, and the top and bottom fibers of the beam.

The bending-strength requirements of the columns are often so small as to make the entire frame very flexible. If for functional reasons an unencumbered bay is required, an increase in rigidity of the frame can be achieved only by increasing the bending rigidity of its columns. On the other hand, rigidity is inexpensively obtained by tensile or compressive elements: hence, tensile or compressive diagonals may be used to stiffen the frame with little increase in material (Fig. 8.13). In general, structural systems with rectangular meshes, such as frames, are more flexible than triangulated systems, but triangulated systems seldom meet the functional requirements of a modern building.

8.3 Multiple Frames

The advantages of continuity can be compounded by the use of **multiple frames,** in which a horizontal beam is supported by, and rigidly connected to, three or more columns.

In view of the rigidity of compressed elements (see Section 5.2), the vertical deflections of the columns of a multiple frame are small, and the behavior of its beam, when loaded vertically, is similar to, although not identical with, that of a continuous beam on rigid supports (see Section 7.3). Under the action of loads concentrated on one span, the multiple frame develops curvatures not only in all other spans, as a continuous beam, but in all columns as well. The frame as a whole also exhibits a lateral displacement, the so-called **sidesway,** which is absent in the continuous beam (Fig. 8.14).

If the spans and the loads of the multiple frame do not differ substantially from bay to bay, the thrusts in adjoining frames act in opposite directions

178

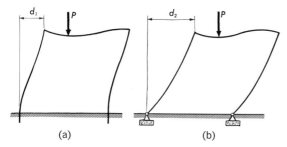

(a)   (b)

8.12 Deformation of hinged and fixed
frames under unsymmetrical load.

P_w

8.13 Diagonally stiffened frame.

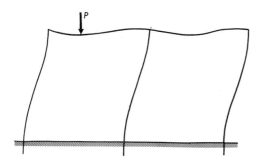

P

8.14 Sidesway of multiple frame.

and tend to cancel each other. Theoretically only the two outer bays need be tied or buttressed. In practice, some means must always be provided to take care of uneven loadings on the various spans of the multiple frame: the excess thrust is often resisted by the foundations.

Multiple frames are efficient in absorbing lateral loads. The rigidity of the beam against compressive loads makes the lateral deflections of the tops of all the columns practically identical. Hence, the lateral load is carried equally by all the equal columns of the frame, each acting as a cantilever and additionally stiffened by the bending rigidity of the beam. The overturning tendency due to wind action is equilibrated by tensile forces on the frame columns on the windward side, and by compressive forces on the leeward side. In view of the greater number of column forces and their increased lever arms, these forces are relatively small. Multiple frames in the external walls of a building are often used to carry the wind load on the faces perpendicular to these walls.

A single-bay frame with a beam rigidly connecting the foot of the columns is a closed structural element capable of carrying vertical and horizontal loads [Fig. 8.15(a)]. A multiple-bay frame with continuous beams at the top and the bottom of the columns is also a closed system, and may be used as a truss to span large distances [Fig. 8.15(b)]. In this case, the multiple frame may be thought of as a beam with compression and tension flanges, in which the shear is carried by the columns. The bending stresses in the horizontal and vertical elements of such truss-frames are much greater than in the members of triangulated trusses, but the simplicity of their connections and their unencumbered bays have made these truss-frames popular. **Vierendeel trusses,** named after their Belgian inventor, are commonly used in bridge design. They are also used in buildings when the structure is supported on wide spans and unencumbered bays are essential. In this case, the truss consists actually of the columns and floor beams of the building (Fig. 8.16).

180

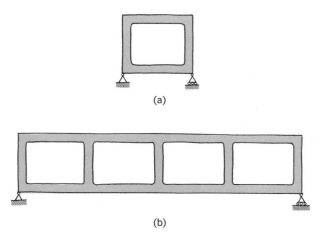

(a)

(b)

8.15 Vierendeel truss and bridge.

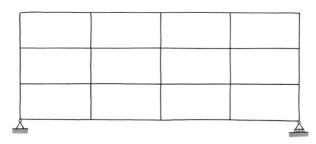

8.16 Vierendeel-truss structure.

Multistory frames with superimposed bays are commonly used in tall structures. Their action against vertical loads is similar to that of single-bay frames, with the added advantage that the horizontal beams act both as load-carrying elements for a given floor and as tie-rods for the frame above it.

The action of a single-bay, multistory frame under lateral loads is similar to the action of a cantilevered Vierendeel truss: the leeward columns are in compression and bending, the windward columns in tension and bending, while the floor beams and slabs transmit the shear from the tension to the compression elements (Fig. 8.17). One may also think of the frame as a gigantic I-beam, cantilevered from the ground, in which the depth equals the width of the frame and the floor beams act as web. The continuity between the floor beams and the columns introduces bending in both the horizontal and the vertical elements, making the entire structure monolithic. A concentrated vertical load is felt in the entire structure, each part of which collaborates in carrying it (Fig. 8.18).

As the height and the width of the building increase, it becomes practical to increase the number of bays so as to reduce the beam spans and to absorb horizontal loads more economically. The resisting structure of the building thus becomes a frame with a number of rectangular meshes, allowing free circulation inside the building, and capable of resisting both vertical and horizontal loads. A number of such frames, parallel to each other and connected by horizontal beams, constitute the cage structures encountered in most steel or concrete buildings today. These **three-dimensional frames** act integrally against horizontal loads coming from any direction, since their columns may be considered as part of either system of frames at right angles to each other (Fig. 8.19).

8.17 Multistory frame under lateral loads.

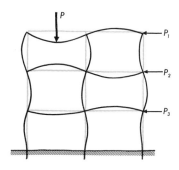

8.18 Multistory frame under concentrated load (sidesway prevented).

8.19 Three-dimensional frame.

The skyscraper is one of the great conquests of modern structural design, made possible by the multistory frame and the high strength of steel and concrete. The Empire State Building, to this day the highest building in the world, although built in 1930, has 102 floors and is 1472 feet high, including the 200-foot upper tower originally designed to anchor dirigibles, and the 222-foot TV antenna. Concrete skyscrapers cannot reach the height of steel skyscrapers, but are found to be economical for heights of up to 600 feet; the tallest built to date (the Marina towers in Chicago) is over 600 feet high.

A skyscraper is nothing but a slender, vertical, cantilevered beam resisting lateral and vertical loads. The vertical floor loads accumulate from the top to the bottom of the building, requiring larger columns as one moves down. Were it not for the high compressive strength of modern structural materials, the area of the columns would encroach on the usable floor area to the point where this might become nil.

The efficiency of frame action is required by skyscrapers to absorb horizontal wind loads. A wind pressure of 30 pounds per square foot represents a total load of approximately 5 million pounds on the 1472-foot cantilever of the Empire State Building. Under the action of the wind load the top of the building sways a few inches.

The columns and beams of a framed structure are its resisting "skeleton." In order to enclose the space defined by the skeleton and to make it usable,

184

the exterior of the building is covered with a "skin" and the floor areas are spanned by horizontal floor systems. The skin of modern buildings is often made of metal or concrete and glass, and called a **curtain wall.** The floor structure consists of long-span beams connecting the main frames, of secondary beams or joists spanning the distance between the main beams, and of slabs of concrete or steel decks, spanning the distance between the secondary beams. Such systems are analyzed in Chapter 10.

8.4 Gabled Frames and Arches

All three members of a single-bay frame under vertical loads are subjected to compressive **and** bending stresses. The columns are compressed by the loads on the beam and bent by the rotation of the joint connecting them rigidly to the beam. The beam is bent by the loads and compressed by the thrust from the foot of the columns. With the usual proportions of beam and columns, compression prevails in the columns and bending in the beams. The columns are relatively slender and the beam is relatively deep.

Whenever for functional reasons the top member of the frame must be horizontal, this type of design is efficient and economical, but it may be improved when the upper member may be curved. In **gabled frames** the top member consists of two inclined beams. If these were hinged at top and bottom, they would act as the compressed struts of a triangular truss, and the columns would be bent by the thrust of the upper member, besides being compressed by its vertical reactions (Fig. 8.20). Continuity between the gable and the columns introduces bending in the gabled member, so that the frame transfers loads by a combination of compression and bending in all its members (Fig. 8.21). The higher the rise of the gable, the larger the compression and the smaller the bending in it. The load-carrying capacity of the gable may be split between the two mechanisms of compression and bending, gaining in efficiency and saving material.

The principle used in gabled frames may be extended. The columns may be shortened and the upper member folded so as to have more than two straight sides, with an increase in compression and a reduction in bending (Fig. 8.22). At its limit, the frame with an infinite number of infinitesimally short sides becomes an **arch.**

It was noted in Section 6.3 that for each set of loads there is a particular arch shape (the so-called funicular shape) for which the entire arch is under simple compression. Such shape can be determined by hanging the loads from a cable and by turning the resulting curve upside-down. Funicular arches are at one end of the stress scale, where there is no bending; beams are at the other, where there is bending only. Any other downward curved structural member will carry loads by a combination of compression and bending. Even if an arch is funicular for **one** set of loads, it cannot be funicular for **all** sets of loads it may have to carry: a combination of compression and bending is always present in an arch.

186

8.20 Hinged gabled frame.

8.21 Continuous gabled frame.

8.22 Polygonal frame.

In masonry design the arch is heavy and loaded by the weight of walls; its shape is usually the funicular of the dead load, and introduces some bending due to live loads. In large steel arches the live load represents a greater share of the total load than in stone arches, and introduces a larger amount of bending; but bending is seldom critical, in view of the tensile strength of steel.

The arch thrust is absorbed by a tie-rod whenever the foundation material is not suitable. When the arch allows the free passage of traffic under it, whether it is a bridge or the arched entrance to a hall, its thrust is absorbed either by buttresses or by tie-rods buried under ground.

The stationary or moving loads carried by the arch of a bridge are usually supported on a horizontal surface. This surface may be above or below the arch, connected to it by compression **struts** [Fig. 8.23(a)] or tension **hangers** [Fig. 8.23(b)]. The compression struts are often restrained laterally against buckling by diagonals or transverse beams, particularly when the arch is deep.

The shape of an arch is not chosen for purely structural reasons. The half circle, exclusively used by the Romans, has construction properties that justify its use. Similarly, the pointed Gothic arch has both visual and structural advantages, while the Arabic arch, typical of the mosques and of some Venetian architecture, is "incorrect" from a purely structural viewpoint (Fig. 8.24).

(a)

(b)

8.23 Bridge structures.

Roman   Gothic   Arabic   **8.24** Arch shapes.

The shape of the arch may be chosen to be as close as possible to the funicular of the heaviest loads, so as to minimize bending. On the other hand, it is often more important to minimize the arch thrust so as to reduce the dimensions of the tie-rod, or to guarantee that the soil will not settle excessively under the pressure of the abutments. The thrust may be shown to be proportional to the total load and to the span, and inversely proportional to the rise of the arch. To minimize the thrust for a given distance to be spanned, the arch must be as light as possible, and have a rise as high as economically feasible (Fig. 8.25).

The arch may have hinged or fixed supports. The hinged supports allow the rotation of the arch abutments under load and under temperature changes. Hinged arches are relatively flexible, and do not develop high bending stresses under temperature variations or soil settlements. Steel hinges are used at the abutments of most steel arches [Fig. 8.7(a)]. Reinforced-concrete hinges were developed by the French engineer Mesnagier, who first crossed the reinforcing bars to create a section where the bending resistance was substantially weakened by the lack of lever arm for the steel bars [Fig. 8.7(b)].

Fixed arches are built both in steel and in concrete. They are stiffer than hinged arches, and consequently are more sensitive to temperature stresses and settlements of the supports.

If temperature or settlement stresses are to be entirely avoided, a third hinge may be introduced, usually at the **crown** of the arch: the **three-hinge arch** is entirely free to "breathe" or to settle unevenly without bending deformation of its two halves (Fig. 8.26). Such arches, commonly used at the end of the nineteenth century, have lost their popularity because of the improved knowledge of arch behavior.

190

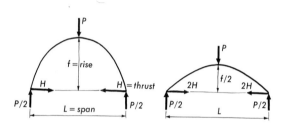

8.25 Variation of arch thrust with rise.

8.26 Three-hinge arch displacements.

When bending materials were costly and easily deteriorated by adverse weather conditions, the arch was the structural member most commonly used to span even modest distances. Roman and Romanesque architecture are immediately recognized by the circular arch motive. The Gothic, high-rise arch and the buttresses required to absorb its thrust are typical of one of the greatest achievements in architectural design, the Gothic cathedral (Fig. 8.27). In these magnificent structures, built of a material capable of resisting compression only, a combination of arches channels to the ground the loads of roofs spanning up to one hundred feet. The high rise of the arch reduces the thrust, and lightened buttresses, in the shape of half-arches, channel it to points where the weight of the heavy columns helps absorb it. A Gothic cathedral is essentially a framed building in which the curved frame elements develop almost exclusively compressive stresses.

8.27 Section of Gothic cathedral.

8.28 The longest steel arch in the world.

It was only with the development of bending resisting materials that greater structural achievements were obtained. Roman circular arches spanned about 100 feet, medieval stone bridges up to 180 feet. The Kill van Kull Bridge in the United States is the largest single arch span in steel to date and spans 1652 feet (Fig. 8.28). The largest single arch span in reinforced concrete built to date is the Sando Bridge in Sweden and spans 866 feet (Fig. 8.29). Combinations of arches with cantilevered half-arches connected by trusses have been built to span as much as 1800 feet in the Quebec Bridge (Fig. 8.30). To this day no other structural element is as commonly used to span large distances as the arch.

194

8.29 The longest reinforced concrete arch in the world.

8.30 The longest cantilever span in the world.

8.5 Arched Roofs

It was seen in the previous section that the roof of a Gothic cathedral is a combination of arches, capable of channeling the roof load to the ground. Arches are used in a variety of combinations to support curved roofs. One of the simplest is a series of parallel arches connected by transverse elements and roofed by plates, which constitute a **barrel roof** (Fig. 8.31). The connecting elements transmit the roof load to the arches by bending or arch action, and these channel the load to the ground mostly by compression. This is the mechanism used in the medieval, Romanesque church roofs, and in the modern cylindrical concrete hangars, first built in the United States in the 1940's. The shape of the arches is chosen to be the funicular of the dead load; any additional load due to wind or snow produces a certain amount of bending in the arches. The element connecting the arches is a brick vault in the medieval churches, and a concrete curved plate in the modern hangars. Barrel roofs supported by steel arches are also common in modern factory roof design.

Rectangular areas are often covered by structures in which the arches span the diagonals rather than the sides of the rectangle (Fig. 8.32). Typical of this kind of structure are the vaults over the transept of medieval churches, and some reinforced-concrete structures used in large halls, as the air terminal at St. Louis, Missouri, designed by Yamasaki.

196

8.31 Arched barrel roof.

8.32 Diagonal-arch roof.

Circular or otherwise curved boundary areas may be covered by arches converging toward the center of the curved area, as in some Gothic chapels or modern wood roofs (Fig. 8.33). In this case the arches butt against a central ring or plate, and their action is more integral than in the case of parallel arches. Arched domes have been used in modern times as roofs of exceptionally large halls for a variety of functional purposes (see Chapter 12).

In the **lamella roof** structure a series of parallel arches, skewed with respect to the sides of the rectangular covered area, is intersected by another series of skew arches so that an efficient interaction is obtained between them (Fig. 8.34). This system does away with the beams connecting parallel arches and constitutes a **curved space frame.** It is particularly efficient when the lengths of the sides of the rectangle do not differ appreciably, since in this case the arches near the corners have small spans and are very rigid, thus reducing the effective span length of the arches butting into them. Lamella roofs of wood, of steel, and of concrete are used to create barrel-shaped roofs. Among the largest concrete roofs of this kind are the hangar roofs designed and built by Nervi in the 1940's, which spanned 1080 feet by 427 feet and consisted of prefabricated concrete elements connected by welding the reinforcing bars at the mesh points of the roof and by concreting the joints. None of these hangars exists today, since they were dynamited during the Second World War, but it is interesting to notice that after being dropped to the ground from a height of 40 feet, these roofs remained integral, except for a few among many hundreds of joints.

8.33 Radial-arch roof.

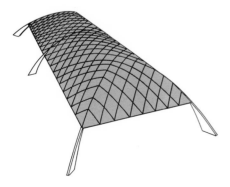

8.34 Lamella roof.

Chapter Nine

Some Fine Points of Structural Behavior

9.1 How Simple is Simple Stress?

The structural systems considered in the previous chapters react to external loads with states of stress called "simple." A cable develops "simple tension," a funicular arch "simple compression," a beam "simple bending," or "simple bending" combined with "simple shear." A more careful look at the ways in which loads are actually carried by even the simplest element will prove, instead, that the stresses developed in a structure are most of the time anything but simple.

If a weight is to be suspended from a cable, a connection must be developed between the weight and the cable. One of the devices most commonly used to achieve this purpose is called a "conical connector," and consists of a short cylinder with a slightly tapered inner surface, within which are located three conical segments (Fig. 9.1). The cable is gripped by the three segments, which are pulled into the cylinder by the friction developed between the cable and the segments; the larger the pull of the cable, the greater the friction developed. The greater friction pulls the segments deeper into the cylinder, and they develop a tighter grip on the cable. The conical connector is a self-locking device.

The section of cable gripped by the connector is acted upon by frictional shears parallel to its surface, and by compressive stresses perpendicular to its surface (Fig. 9.2). The compressive stresses squeeze the cable, and the frictional shears actually transfer the load from the cable in tension to the connector. In the neighborhood of the connector the stresses in the cable present a complicated pattern of compression and surface shear, but they **rapidly** merge into a simple-tension pattern away from the connector (Fig. 9.2).

9.1 Conical connector.

9.2 Stresses in cable due to conical connector.

As proved by the French engineer de St. Venant, the tendency of complicated stress patterns to **become** simple occurs often in correctly designed structural elements, and justifies the elementary approach to stress used in the preceding sections. The stresses in the portion of cable gripped by the connector are complicated, but at a distance from the connector equal to two or three times the diameter of the cable, the stress pattern, to all practical purposes, is one of simple tension. The cable is designed for simple tension because only a small portion of it is under a more complicated state of stress. On the other hand, the stresses in the portion of cable gripped by the connector may be much higher, and of a more dangerous kind than simple tension, and cannot be ignored.

A condition similar to that existing in the cable arises in a truss bar under tension. The connection between the bar and the gusset plate is often riveted. The rivets develop compressive stresses on the inner surface of the bar holes, and shears due to friction on the plate surface; these stresses are transformed into simple tension away from the connection (Fig. 9.3). Truss bars are designed as if they were under simple tension or compression, but the complicated stress pattern in the neighborhood of the gusset plate must be taken into careful account.

204

(a)

(b)

9.3 Stresses in riveted joint.

9.2 The Largest Stress

It was shown in Section 5.3 that pure shear is equivalent to compression and tension at right angles. Some essential implications of these equivalent states of stress must now be considered.

Since shear stresses develop on the horizontal and vertical sides of a rectangular element cut out of a beam, and hence tension and compression on the sides of a rectangular element at 45 degrees to the horizontal, one may inquire as to what stresses are developed on the side AB of a rectangular element oriented to any other angle (Fig. 9.4). It seems natural to investigate **how the stress varies as the rectangular element rotates,** since for an angle equal to zero (horizontal position of the side AB) the stress is pure shear, for an angle of 45 degrees it becomes compression, for an angle of 90 degrees it is shear again, and for an angle of 135 degrees it becomes tension.

A general analysis of this question shows that, whatever the stress pattern, as the element rotates: (a) the direct stress varies from a maximum to a minimum value; (b) the maximum and minimum direct stresses are at right angles to each other; (c) **shear is never developed** on the sides of the element for which **the direct stress is maximum or minimum;** (d) both shear **and** direct stress are developed for any other orientation of the sides. In the elementary case of "simple shear," the maximum stress is tension (equal in magnitude to the shear) at an angle of 135 degrees, the minimum stress is compression (considered as **negative** tension) at an angle of 45 degrees; and there is no shear on these elements.

The perpendicular directions for which the stresses become maximum or minimum are called the **principal directions;** the corresponding values of the stresses are called their **principal values.**

206

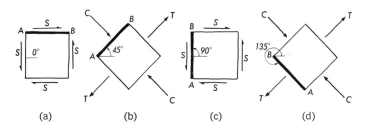

(a) (b) (c) (d)

9.4 Stress variation with orientation of element.

The principal directions of stress allow a visualization of complex stress patterns. In general, the two principal directions vary from point to point of a stress pattern and may be indicated by small crosses (Fig. 9.5). Lines may, then, be drawn parallel to the principal directions at each point of the stress pattern. There are two families of such lines and they intersect at right angles (Fig. 9.5); they are called the **principal stress lines, or isostatic lines.** The stress-lines pattern indicates the flow of stress within the structural element, and is useful in visualizing dangerous stress situations.

Figure 9.6 illustrates the stress lines in a dam loaded by the pressure of water on its vertical side. Since water exerts only normal pressure on the vertical wall, the dam elements at the wall do not develop shear. Hence, the principal stress directions at the wall are vertical and horizontal. One family of isostatics starts horizontally at this wall. The inclined wall is altogether free of stress, and, in particular, of shear stress. Hence the direction of the inclined wall is one of the principal directions there, and the other is perpendicular to it. The heavy stress lines show how the pressure of the water is channeled down the dam so as to become perpendicular to the dam foundation. The light stress lines of the second family cross the compression lines at right angles, and show that in these directions the dam acts as a series of cables in tension. Thus, the action of the dam is seen to be a combination of tension and compression at right angles, in varying directions.

208

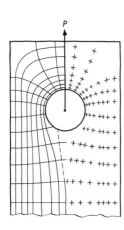

9.5 Principal stress lines or isostatics.

9.6 Isostatics of dam.

9.7 (a) Isostatics of tension bar.　　　(a)

The stress lines for a flat bar in simple tension constitute a mesh of vertical lines, and of horizontal compressive lines due to Poisson's phenomenon (see Section 5.1) [Fig. 9.7(a)]. If a hole is introduced in the bar, the straight tensile lines cannot go through the hole, and are diverted around it. In so doing the tensile stress lines crowd in the neighborhood of the hole, and the compression lines bend so as to remain perpendicular to the tension lines [Fig. 9.7(b)]. The flow of the tensile stresses is similar to the flow of water in a river: the flow pattern is made up of parallel lines when the river banks are parallel and there is no obstruction in the river, but the lines curve when a circular pile is embedded in the current, compelling the water to move around the pile. The similarity between these two flow patterns is quite significant: just as the water

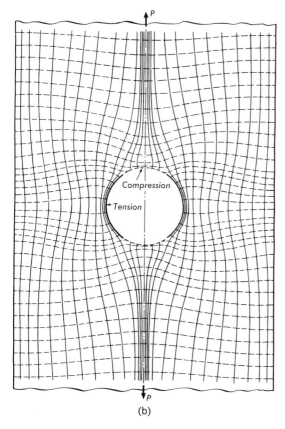

9.7 (b) Isostatics of tension bar with hole.

of the river increases its speed to move through the restricted section created by the obstruction, the tensile stress increases its value because of the obstruction created by the hole. Thus, the tensile stress across the two sections at the sides of the hole is not uniform, but higher near the hole than at the boundary of the bar (Fig. 9.8). Such increases in stress due to holes, sharp notches, and other abrupt changes in cross section are called **stress concentrations.** Stress concentrations may increase the value of the stress above its average value by large factors, thus bringing the stress not only above the elastic limit, but above the ultimate strength of the material. For example, when the edge of a piece of material is nicked, a high stress concentration is developed under tension, and the material tears as the stress concentration moves along the cut. Without the nick, it is practically impossible to tear the material.

Figure 9.9(a) gives the stress lines for a simply supported beam under uniform load. The bending and shear stress pattern considered in previous sections is shown by the stress lines to be equivalent to a set of arch stresses, indicated by the heavy compression lines, combined with a set of cable stresses, indicated by the light tension lines, at right angles to each other. The bottom fiber of the beam is in tension, and if a notch is cut out of the beam at midspan, stress concentration arises, because the tensile stress lines must go around the notch and crowd at its top [Fig. 9.9(b)]. When the load on a beam, made of a material stronger in compression than in tension, is increased beyond safe values, the more efficient arch action carries more of the load as the fibers in tension fail. Thus, the beam at first carries the load by bending but changes its mechanism to compression as soon as failure in tension makes bending impossible. This readjustment of stress cannot be counted upon for normal loads, since it is accompanied by large displacements and the partial failure of the beam, but is useful in preventing or retarding the total collapse of a structure under exceptional loads.

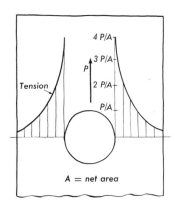

9.8 Stress concentration in tension bar.

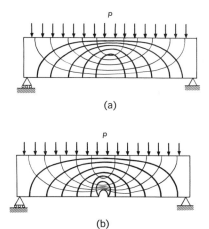

(a)

(b)

9.9 Isostatics of simply supported beam.

9.3 The Importance of Plastic Flow

It was stated in Section 3.1 that most structural materials have an elastic stress range, followed by a plastic range, and that under normal loading conditions stresses are kept below the elastic limit in order to avoid the accumulation of permanent deformations, which may occur through plastic flow. On the other hand, plastic flow plays an essential role in the behavior of all structural elements.

In the post-and-lintel system it is generally assumed that the lintel rests on the post, and that a uniform compression is developed between their contact surfaces. This assumption would be correct if the two surfaces were ideally smooth; in practice, instead, both are uneven and present small irregular bumps. If two bumps coincide (Fig. 9.10), the contact is limited to a small area and the compressive stress on it may be many times greater than if the contact took place over the entire surface. But, if the high stress developed at the bumps is above the yield point, the material flows, the bumps flatten, the contact area increases, and the stress decreases to acceptable values. Thus, **plastic flow eliminates stress concentrations** due to the roughness of the surfaces, and brings about a stress situation nearer the ideal one on which the design was based. Posts and lintels of brittle materials (see Section 3.1) could not readjust, and would fail owing to the high stress concentrations.

Besides the unavoidable presence of small irregularities, another cause of stress concentration exists at the inner edge of the post. As the lintel bends under the applied loads it tends to rest on the inner portion of the contact area with the post, and, at the limit, on its inner edge alone [Fig. 9.11(a)]. If the post were made of a hard material, the partial contact would increase the contact stresses and the edge of the post would cut into the lintel. In practice, plastic flow comes to the rescue. The rotation of the lintel produces a stress concentration at the inner edge of the post, and the material of the post flows together with the lintel material. Plastic flow increases the contact areas between these two elements until the stresses are reduced to acceptable values, and flow stops [Fig. 9.11(b)].

214

(a)   (b)

9.10 Stress concentration and flow.

(a)   (b)

9.11 Redistribution of stress by flow.

The stress concentrations at the ends of the horizontal diameter of the hole in the tension bar (Fig. 9.8) are similarly relieved by plastic flow. In the neighborhood of these points flow spreads until the stress lines acquire greater radii of curvature, and do not crowd as much as they did when compelled to go around a hole of small radius. The analogy with the flow of water may be carried one step further: in order to reduce the pressure on the piles of a bridge, piling guards are set up which divert the flow of water in a smoother fashion. The plastic areas (Fig. 9.12) around the stress concentration points perform the same role, and ease the stress flow of elastic stresses.

Stress redistribution due to plastic flow is responsible for the **reserve of strength** exhibited by beams, frames, and other structures in which loads are carried essentially in bending. It was found in Section 7.2 that the midspan section of a simply supported beam develops the highest bending stresses under symmetrical loads. The heaviest loads the beam can safely carry are those for which the upper and lower fibers at midspan are stressed up to the allowable stress for the given material. If the extreme fiber stresses reach the elastic limit [Fig. 9.13(a)], the stress distribution through the beam depth is still linear and all but the extreme fibers are stressed below the elastic limit.

If the loads on the beam are increased further, the extreme fiber stresses cannot grow any higher, since the elastic limit is practically the value of the stress at which plastic flow starts; but the other beam fibers may help support the additional loads by increasing **their** stress up to the elastic limit. The stress distribution in the beam stops being triangular, and follows the diagram of Fig. 9.13(b). The loads may be increased until **all** fibers reach the elastic limit, at which point the stress distribution is rectangular [Fig. 9.13(c)], the beam reaches its **ultimate load** capacity, and **all** fibers flow, the upper fibers in compression and the lower in tension. The beam fails at this point,

216

9.12 Plastic flow at edge of hole in tension bar.

9.13 Plastic flow in beam section.

because its two halves rotate about the middle section **as if the beam had a hinge at midspan,** and a three-hinge beam is a moving mechanism (Fig. 9.14). For a rectangular cross-section the ultimate load is 50 per cent higher than the load at which flow starts; plastic flow introduces a 50 per cent reserve of strength which might prevent collapse in case of exceptional loads.

A simply supported I-beam is more efficient in bending than a rectangular beam, but does not have such reserve of strength. The I-beam is efficient **because** most of its area is concentrated in the top and bottom flanges, where the stresses are highest. As soon as the flanges flow, the only fibers that can help carry additional loads by increasing their stresses are those in the web; but the web has such a small area that the corresponding increase in load is negligible. Practically, the I-beam develops a **plastic hinge** as soon as the flanges reach the elastic limit; it has no reserve of strength against collapse, because it cannot redistribute stresses in a section.

The reserve of strength is greater for beams with fixed ends. It was seen in Section 7.3 that a fixed-end beam under uniform load develops the highest bending stresses at the supports. If the load is increased beyond the value that brings such stresses up to the elastic limit, the fibers of the end sections flow progressively until, for a beam with rectangular cross section, the stress distribution at the end sections is that shown in Fig. 9.13(c). At this point the end sections (a) have developed **plastic hinges** (Fig. 9.15). As the load keeps increasing, the beam, although originally fixed, behaves as if it were hinged at the ends, and the stresses at the middle section (b) start increasing until they progressively reach the elastic limit. At this point the beam develops three **plastic hinges,** reaches its ultimate capacity, and collapses (Fig. 9.15). It is thus seen that a rectangular cross-section beam with fixed ends has a two-fold source of strength reserve: the plastic flow of the end sections, and the plastic flow of the middle section. The ultimate load for such a beam is twice the load at which flow starts at the extreme fibers of the end sections. Such a beam has a reserve of strength of 100 per cent.

218

9.14 Plastic hinge in simply supported beam.

9.15 Plastic hinges in fixed beam.

An I-beam of constant cross section cannot redistribute stresses **in a section,** but has a reserve of strength of 33 per cent when its ends are fixed. As soon as the flanges of the end sections reach the elastic limit and develop hinges, the stresses in the flanges of the midspan section grow until they develop a third hinge. Additional loads are carried by the increase in stress at midspan. Redistribution of stress occurs **between end and midspan sections,** although not at any **one** section.

Stress redistribution due to plastic flow occurs in any framed structure, since the loads produce maximum stresses only at some critical sections; as soon as one of these sections develops a plastic hinge, stresses start growing at other sections. Continuity between the various bars of a frame allows such redistributions to occur at a number of sections (Fig. 9.16). Thus, continuity insures strength reserve, and develops in the frame a "democratic structural action''; understressed sections come to the help of more severely stressed ones as soon as these have reached their ultimate capacity. Continuity is one of the best guarantees against collapse, even if, under certain loads, it may produce higher elastic stresses at particular points.

Large amounts of flow should usually be avoided, since they introduce permanent, and often increasing, deformations in the structure. On the other hand, small amounts of plastic flow are necessary to smooth out local stress concentrations, which otherwise might endanger the structure. Plastic flow is the mechanism through which a structure redistributes stresses and is made safe against a sudden collapse. It is thus clear that no material may be properly used structurally unless it exhibits some plastic flow under high loads.

9.16 Plastic hinges in simple frame.

Chapter Ten

Grids, Plates, and Folded Plates

10.1 Load Transfer in Two Directions

The structural elements considered so far have in common the property of transferring loads in one direction. A load set on a cable or a beam is channeled to the supports along the cable line or the beam axis; an arch, a frame, and a continuous beam produce the same type of "one-directional load dispersal." These structures are labeled **one-dimensional resisting structures,** because they can be described by a straight or curved line, along which the stresses channel the loads. (Lines are said to have only one dimension, because a **single** number—for example, the distance from one end of the line —is sufficient to define the position of a point on a line.)

One-dimensional resisting elements may be used to cover a rectangular area, but such an arrangement is usually impractical and inefficient. For example, a series of beams, all parallel to one of the sides of the rectangle, serves this purpose; but a concentrated load on such a system is carried entirely by the beam under the load, while all other beams are unstressed (Fig. 10.1). The system is impractical because one beam deflects while the other beams remain horizontal, and inefficient because it does not work as a whole in carrying the load. The load transfer occurs always in the direction of the beams, and the loads are supported by the two walls at their ends, while the walls parallel to the beams remain unloaded. This is a proper solution when unloaded walls are needed for functional purposes, but it becomes uneconomical when the four walls enclosing the space can be used to support loads.

These considerations suggest that it would be structurally more efficient to have "two-way load dispersal." Such dispersal is obtained by means of **grids** and **plates, two-dimensional resisting structures** acting in a plane.

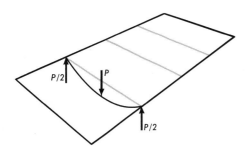

10.1 Concentrated load on one-dimensional system.

10.2 Rectangular Beam Grids

If two identical, simply supported beams, at right angles to each other, are placed one on top of the other, and a concentrated load is applied at their intersection, the load is transferred to the supports at the ends of **both** beams and **dispersed in two directions** (Fig. 10.2). This mechanism involves the loading of the upper beam and its consequent deflection, the deflection of the lower beam by the action of the upper one, and the distribution of the load-carrying action between the two beams. Since the upper beam rests on the lower, the two beams are bound to have the same deflection; and because they are identical, each must carry half the load (Fig. 10.2). Hence, each support reaction equals one-fourth of the load, and "two-way dispersal" reduces the loads on the supports to one-half the value they would have if only one-way dispersal took place.

Two beams at right angles must deflect by the same amount at their intersection even if they have different lengths or different cross sections. However, a greater load is required to deflect a stiffer beam as much as a more flexible one. Hence, the stiffer beam will absorb a greater share of the load than the more flexible beam, and the loads on the two beams will not be equal. The stiffness of a beam under a concentrated load is inversely proportional to the cube of its length. Thus if two beams of identical cross section have spans in the ratio of one to two, their stiffnesses are in the ratio of eight to one. Consequently, the short beam will carry eight-ninths of the load and the long beam one-ninth of the load (Fig. 10.3).

226

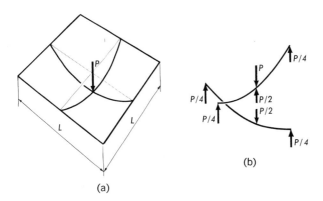

(a)

(b)

10.2 Two-way load dispersal by equal beams.

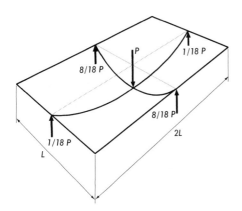

10.3 Two-way dispersal by different beams.

This example shows that the two-way transfer is efficient if the two beams are of equal, or almost equal, stiffness. As soon as one beam is much stiffer than the other, the stiffer beam carries most of the load, and the transfer occurs essentially in one direction. To obtain an efficient two-way transfer in the case of unequal spans, the longer beam must have a substantially stiffer cross section, that is, a greater moment of inertia (see Section 7.1).

The sharing of one concentrated load between two beams may be extended to a series of loads by setting a beam on two or more perpendicular beams, one under each load. Once again, the intersection points must deflect by the same amounts. In the arrangement of Fig. 10.4 the deflections of the unsupported long beam at the quarter points would be smaller than the deflection at midspan. Hence, if the three shorter cross-beams have equal stiffness, the middle beam takes a greater share of the load than the side beams, since it deflects more. For beams of identical cross section, and cross-beams one-half as long as the long beam, the loads at the supports have the values shown in Fig. 10.4. The greater dispersal in the direction of the shorter, stiffer span is evident: the long sides support 94 per cent of the total load. With a long beam eight times stiffer, the long sides still carry about 65 per cent of the total load.

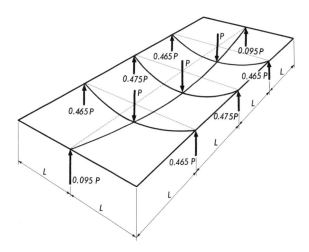

10.4 Two-way dispersal of three loads.

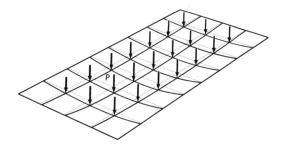

10.5 Rectangular grid.

Finally, one may cover a rectangular area by a **grid** of beams at right angles, and obtain the two-way dispersal of loads located at any grid intersection (Fig. 10.5). If all the beams of the grid running in one direction are set **above** the beams running in the other, any one of the upper beams acts as a continuous beam on flexible supports provided by the lower beams. In this grid an uncentered load may produce upward deflections of an upper beam, and lift it from its supports (Fig. 10.6). A better interaction of the two beam systems is obtained by "weaving" the beams so as to have their relative positions change at each intersection (Fig. 10.7). In this case the grid system is capable of giving support from both below and above: a beam moving up is pulled down by the cross-beam set above it, while a beam moving down is pushed up by the beam under it. In practice, the same result is obtained by means of welded or riveted connections between the two beam systems.

230

10.6 Uplift of upper beam of grid.

10.7 Woven grid.

Rigid connections between the beams of the two systems introduce another structural action in the grid. When two beams connected at midspan are deflected by a concentrated load at their intersection, their midspan sections (a) move downward, but **remain vertical** because of symmetry (Fig. 10.8). When the intersection of the two beams does not occur at midspan, the beam sections (b) deflect and **rotate** (Fig. 10.8). The continuity introduced by the rigid connection transforms the **bending** rotation of one section into a **twisting** rotation of the other. The stiffness of the grid is substantially greater when the beams are rigidly connected than when they are simply supported one over the other; this indicates that the twisting mechanism is capable of transferring part of the load, thus producing smaller displacements in the grid. A grid model in which the beams are "woven" may be used to show that the partially rigid connections introduce a certain amount of twist in the beams, and that the woven grid is stiffer than the unwoven grid.

Grid systems are seen to be particularly efficient in transferring concentrated loads, and in having the entire structure participate in the load-carrying action. This efficiency is reflected not only in the better distribution of the loads over the supports, but in the reduced **depth-to-span ratio** of rectangular grids. Systems of parallel beams used in ordinary construction have depth-to-span ratios of the order of one-tenth to one-twentyfourth. This ratio varies with the beam material. Steel beams may be somewhat shallower than prestressed concrete beams; reinforced concrete beams deeper; wood beams still deeper; but the depth-to-span ratio cannot go much below one-twentyfourth, if the beams are to be practically acceptable from the viewpoint of strength and of deflection. Rectangular grid systems may be economically designed with depth-to-span ratios of as little as one-thirtieth to one-fortieth. When accumulated over a large number of floors, this reduction in depth lowers structural and other costs, by reducing the height of the building.

The substitution of trusses for beams transforms grids into **space frames,** which exhibit the same two-dimensional behavior (see Section 6.5).

232

(b) Twist   (a) No twist   (b)

10.8 Grid action without and with twist.

10.9 Skew grid.

10.3 Skew Grids

An additional saving in floor depths and total building costs may be achieved by the use of skew grids, in which the beams do not run parallel but at an angle to the sides of the base rectangle (Fig. 10.9). The advantages thus obtained are twofold.

In the case of rectangular areas with one side much longer than the other, the two beam systems of a skew grid do not span widely different distances, and the loss of two-way action is greatly reduced. Moreover, the beams diagonally across the corners of a rectangle are shorter and stiffer than the other beams, and give stronger support to the beams crossing them. For loads concentrated around the center of the plate, and even for uniformly distributed loads, these stiff supports create a reversal of curvature in the longer beams, which behave very much as if they were fixed at the ends rather than simply supported (Fig. 10.10). Since a fixed beam has a load carrying capacity for uniform loads 50 per cent greater than an identical simply supported beam, skew grids have greater structural efficiency. Their depth-to-span ratios are often as low as one-fortieth to one-sixtieth.

Space frames are also built on the principle of the skew grid. The skew-crossing arches of the **lamella roofs** extend the grid principle to curved elements (Fig. 10.11). The rigidity of the connections introduces torsion in the arches, thus adding another load-carrying mechanism to their compression and bending mechanisms.

234

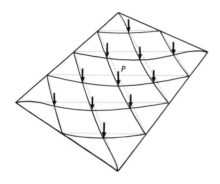

10.10 Reversal of curvature in skew grids.

10.11 Lamella roof.

10.4 **Plates**

The two-way action of beam grids is due to the pointwise connection of the two beam systems at their intersections. Such action is even more pronounced in practice, because the holes of the grid are plugged with slabs or plates, thus making the roof or floor an almost monolithic structure. The advantages of an entirely monolithic structure having two-way action **at all points** would be even more pronounced.

A **plate** or **slab** is a monolithic structural element of relatively small depth covering an area, which at first shall be assumed to be rectangular. Any strip of plate parallel to one side of the rectangle may be thought of as a beam acting in that direction; any strip at right angles to the first may also be considered as a beam, and since the two perpendicular beams act together, bending of one produces twisting in the other [Fig. 10.12(a)]. The action of a plate is analogous to that of a welded beam grid with an infinite number of beams infinitesimally near to one another; but the beams of the grid may be considered to act in **any** direction, since the plate may be ideally divided into strips connecting any two points on its boundary [Fig. 10.12(b)]. Since, moreover, in any physical phenomenon nature follows the easiest path, structural elements tend to carry loads by their most efficient mechanism, and a plate acts as **the** set of welded grid beams transferring the load to the supports by means of the **lowest** possible stresses. A plate distributes the load between the supports in the most economical manner.

The analogy with a beam grid shows that a plate under load will deflect and twist at every point. The deflections produce beam-action **in two directions,** that is, bending and shear stresses; twisting produces torsional shears (see Section 5.3).

236

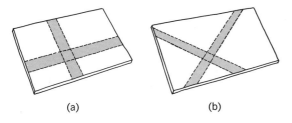

(a)   (b)

10.12 Equivalent grids in plate action.

It is easy to visualize the role of bending, shear, and torsional stresses in the transmission of a concentrated load by plate action. If the plate consisted of a series of independent parallel beams, only the beam under load would deflect, thus transferring the load to the supports by bending and shear [Fig. 10.13(a)]. But the "beams" of a plate are all cemented together so that the loaded beam pulls down the two adjacent parallel beams and transfers **part** of the load to them. This transfer occurs through the shears developed between the vertical sides of the adjacent beams, and produces bending and shear in the adjoining beams [Fig. 10.13(b)]. The two adjacent beams, in turn, transfer **some** of their load to the next beams through shear; the **difference** between the shears coming **from** the loaded beam and those transferred **to** the adjoining beam produces the twisting action [Fig. 10.13(c)]. Thus, a combination of shearing and twisting transfers load at **right angles** to the loaded beam, while bending and shear transfers load **in** the direction of the loaded beam. Since a plate may be considered as a grid of beams, the transfer mechanism takes place not in one but in two directions, and plate action is equivalent to beam action in two directions **plus** twisting action [Fig. 10.13(d)].

Load carrying by twisting action characterizes plates, and differentiates them from beams and grids, since even welded grids cannot develop substantial twisting action. In this connection, it is interesting to notice that the plate twist is responsible for a good percentage of its load-carrying capacity. For example, in a square plate uniformly loaded and simply supported along its four sides, twisting action is responsible for 50 per cent of the load transfer to the supports. In a rectangular grid incapable of developing twist 100 per cent of the load is transferred by bending action.

238

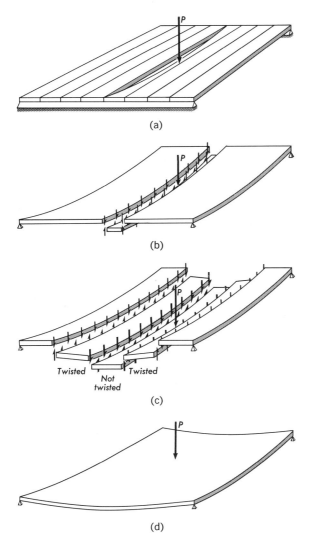

(a)

(b)

Twisted   Twisted

Not
twisted

(c)

(d)

10.13 Plate action.

It was noticed above that a plate may be considered capable of developing grid action in any direction. This means that any point in the plate may be considered as the intersection of two beams of a rectangular grid system, and that any number of rectangular grid systems may be thought of as passing through a plate point [Fig. 10.12(b)]. The bending stresses at a point will vary, depending on the direction of the grid system, because the beam spans to reach the boundaries change with the beam directions. The evaluation of the bending stresses **at a point** shows that there are two directions for which the bending stresses are, respectively, maximum and minimum, and for which the shears are zero. These are the **principal directions,** which were encountered in other stress situations earlier (see Section 9.2). Indicating the principal directions at various points in the plate by crosses, one may plot the **principal stress lines** or **isostatics,** which give the flow of bending stresses in the plate. Since no shear is developed along the isostatics, the plate may also be thought of as a grid of **curved** beams, which meet at right angles, but do not transmit loads to the adjoining beams by shearing action. The isostatics for a simply supported square plate under uniform load are shown in Fig. 10.14(a) and for a rectangular plate in Fig. 10.14(b).

240

(a)

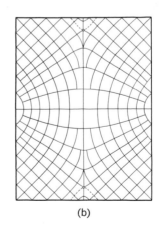

(b)

10.14 Isostatics of simply supported plates under uniform load.

The deflections of the plate of Fig. 10.14(a), shown in Fig. 10.15, explain visually the structural behavior of the plate. The center strips of the plate deflect very much as simply supported beams. At the corners, the two sides of the plate are compelled to remain horizontal, and the entire corner area is stiff; the ends of the diagonal strips are thus prevented from rotating, and behave as fixed-end beams with a reversal of curvature at the ends.

A peculiarity of plate behavior occurs at the corners. If a square plate is supported over a square hole so that the boundaries can provide only **upward**-acting reactions, the plate corners curl up [Fig. 10.16(a)]. In order to have the entire plate boundary in contact with the supports, the corners must be pushed down by concentrated corner forces, which must be added to the load carried by the plate in computing its support reactions. For a square plate under a load concentrated at the center the four corner forces add about 50 per cent to the total plate load [Fig. 10.16(b)].

The stiffness of a simply supported square plate may be compared to the stiffness of simply supported beams having spans equal to the sides of the plate. The center deflection of the plate is 42 per cent smaller than the corresponding beam deflections. The stresses in the plate are 29 per cent smaller than in the beams. The reversed bending stresses at the corners of the plate are two and a half times smaller than the stresses in the beams of a diagonal system connecting opposite plate corners. Although the bending-stress distribution **across the thickness** of the plate is the linear distribution encountered in bending, and as such is not ideally efficient, the two-way plate action reduces the maximum stresses by substantial amounts.

242

10.15 Deflections of simply supported square plate under uniform load.

(a)

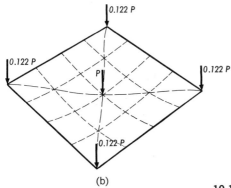

(b)

10.16 Curling up of plate corners.

A knowledge of maximum and minimum stresses, of reversed stresses, and of the directions in which the shear stresses become maximum is essential in placing the reinforcements of concrete plates. Maximum shears always occur in directions at 45 degrees with the principal directions; in the corners of the plate shear acts as shown in Fig. 10.17(a), and the reinforcing bars may be oriented as shown in Fig. 10.17(b) in order to absorb directly the corresponding tensile stress.

It was shown in Section 10.2 that rectangular grid systems lose most of their two-way action as soon as one of the sides of the rectangle is much longer than the other. Plates exhibit the same behavior, as indicated in Fig. 10.18 for the case of a rectangular plate with sides in the ratio of two to one. The center deflection of the plate is only 15 per cent smaller than the deflection of cross-beams parallel to its short sides, since the shorter "beams" carry eight-ninths of the load (see Fig. 10.3). The largest stress in the plate is only 20 per cent smaller than in the short equivalent cross-beam. Most of the load is transferred to the long side supports, since the short span is much stiffer than the long span; the long sides carry two-thirds of the load.

What has been said of plates with simply supported sides may be repeated for plates with fixed sides. Such plates are stiffer and behave like a rectangular, welded grid of fixed beams.

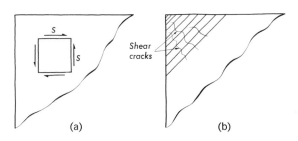

10.17 Shear reinforcement at plate corners.

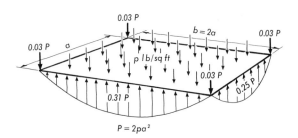

10.18 Action in simply supported rectangular plate.

10.19 Plate with opposite simply supported and fixed sides.

The conditions of support may differ on the four sides of a plate. A plate may have two simply supported parallel sides and two fixed parallel sides. In this case an increased rigidity of the long spans, due to their fixity, may compensate for the large side ratio; the plate exhibits two-way action comparable to that of a square plate with all sides simply supported (Fig. 10.19). Similarly, a plate may have two adjacent sides simply supported and the other two sides completely unsupported. Obviously, no "simply supported" grid could be built in this fashion, since the beams of the lower system would be unsupported. A "woven" grid, instead, would be capable of carrying load mostly by twisting action. The same behavior is exhibited by the plate (Fig. 10.20).

A stiffer plate with two unsupported adjacent sides is obtained by fixing the other two sides (Fig. 10.21); in this case the analogy of a grid system holds, since each beam of the system would be cantilevered, and bending action prevails again.

246

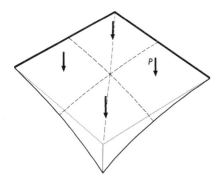

10.20 Plate with adjacent simply supported and free sides.

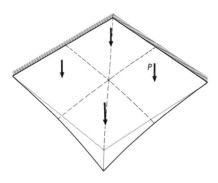

10.21 Plate with two fixed and two free sides.

Rectangular plates may be supported on more than one boundary. In modern office-building design it is common to support the floor plates on an outer wall or a series of columns, and on the inner "core," inside which run the elevators, the air-conditioning ducts, and other parts of the mechanical, electrical, and plumbing systems (Fig. 10.22). A completely free floor area is thus obtained.

The boundary of a plate may have a variety of shapes: instead of covering a rectangle it may cover a skew, a polygonal, or a circular area. The behavior of a circular plate with simply supported boundary does not differ substantially from that of the circumscribed square plate [Fig. 10.23(a)], since the corners of the square plate are rigid and only its central portion presents sizable deflections. The behavior of a circular plate with fixed boundary is similar to that of the inscribed square plate [Fig. 10.23(b)].

Ring plates may be built to span the area limited by an outer and an inner circular support. As soon as the radial span of the plate is small in comparison to its average radius, two-way plate action under uniform load is considerably reduced, and the plate exhibits stresses of the same order of magnitude as those of beams spanning the distance between the two circular boundaries.

248

10.22 Floor plate of building with inner core.

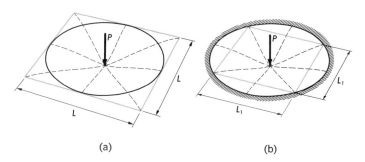

(a)   (b)

10.23 Circular plates.

Plates may also be supported on columns, either hinged or fixed to the plate. The connection between the columns and the plates must be designed to absorb the so-called "punching shear" from the columns, and often requires the use of capitals or of intermediate distributing plates (Fig. 10.24). In order to avoid capitals **shear connectors** of steel are used to guarantee the transmission of load from the column to the plate in reinforced-concrete design (Fig. 10.25).

Plates present the constructional advantage of smooth underside surfaces which permit the unimpeded running of pipes, ducts, and other parts of the various mechanical systems required in a modern building. The savings achieved by the avoidance of pipe and duct bends around the beams often justify the selection of a plate system for floors and roofs.

Reinforced concrete plates supported by steel or concrete columns are easily poured on plane forms. An additional saving in formwork is achieved by pouring the plates on the ground, one on top of the other, and lifting them to the top of the columns by means of hydraulic jacks. Buildings with as many as 15 floors have been built economically by this Lift-slab technique.

Inclined plates are used in roof design, as the sides of gabled roofs, or the sloping sides of "north-light roofs," in which the higher boundary of the plate is supported on a truss (Fig. 10.26). The vertical trussed elements are light, and permit the use of large glass surfaces, usually exposed to the uniform north

10.24 Punching shear in column-supported plate.

Chair

Stub column

10.25 Shear connector.

10.26 Plates in north-light roofs.

light required in factories and artists' studios. Inclined plates are often used in storage bins and other components of industrial buildings (Fig. 10.27). Such inclined plates carry some of the load by tension or compression down their slope, and some by plate action in a direction perpendicular to the plate.

10.5 Ribbed Plates

The structural efficiency of plates is reduced because of the linear stress distribution across their thickness. Only the top and bottom plate fibers at the most stressed **point,** in the most stressed **direction,** may develop allowable stresses. In the case of beams this inefficiency is remedied by locating as much material as possible at a distance from the unstressed neutral axis, thus obtaining I- and T-sections; the same solution can be adopted with plates. Some of the material may be located away from the **neutral middle plane** of the plate, and used to create ribs, which run in one, two, or even three directions (Fig. 10.28). The ribbed plate presents the advantages of continuity due to the slab, and the advantages of depth due to its ribs. On the other hand, the underside of a ribbed plate is not smooth, and a soffit may have to be hung from it. Pipes and ducts are not bent around the ribs but, usually, hung from them.

252

10.27 Inclined plates in storage bins.

10.28 Ribbed plate.

An economical solution of the plate problem for rectangular floors with relatively small spans is often obtained by a mixed structure of reinforced concrete and tiles. The hollow tiles are set on a horizontal scaffolding of planks to create the formwork for parallel reinforced concrete ribs; steel bars are set between the tiles to reinforce the ribs, and above the tiles to reinforce the slab (Fig. 10.29); concrete is then poured in between the tiles and above them. Once the concrete has hardened, the floor acts as a reinforced concrete slab, ribbed in one or two direction, but with a smooth underside due to the tiles. For fairly large spans the portion of the tiles in the compressed areas of the cross section is included in the evaluation of the ribbed-plate strength. Cinder blocks or other insulating material may be used instead of tiles as formwork for the ribbed concrete plate.

A plate ribbed in two perpendicular directions is called a "waffle plate." Waffle plates covering square areas are ribbed with two identical sets of ribs at right angles. When the sides of the rectangular area are substantially different, deeper ribs may be used in one direction or, in the case of reinforced concrete, the two sets of ribs may have the same depth and be reinforced differently (Fig. 10.30). Polygonal and circular plates may also be efficiently ribbed; their ribs usually run in radial and circumferential directions.

254

10.29 Concrete and tile floor.

10.30 Waffle plate.

The appearance of a ribbed plate may be enhanced by following the suggestion of the Italian engineer Arcangeli to have the ribs follow the isostatic lines of the plate (see Section 10.4). The pattern depends on the support conditions at the plate boundary, and on the loads to be carried. For simply supported plates under uniform load the isostatic pattern is often similar to that shown in Fig. 10.14, and was actually used by Nervi in various floor designs (Fig. 10.31). Such curved ribs require expensive forms, and are economically acceptable only if the forms can be reused a number of times.

Steel plates constitute the webs of **plate-girders,** deep beams used in bridges or other large structures. Their buckling resistance is highly increased by vertical or longitudinal stiffeners, which essentially reduce the length of the plate strips that tend to buckle (see Section 7.1). Thus, steel and aluminum webs are often ribbed, not only to increase their direct load-carrying capacity, but to reduce their weakness in buckling (see Fig. 7.25).

10.6 Strength Reserve in Plates

Plates are called **two-dimensional resisting structures** because, in order to define the location of one of their sections, one must give two numbers—say, the distances of the section from its sides, measured parallel to the two sides, in the case of rectangular plates.

One of the essential characteristics of two-dimensional structures is their high reserve of strength, which stems from two separate sources: **stress redistribution** and **membrane action** (see Section 11.2).

256

10.31 Plate ribbed along isostatics.

It was shown in Section 9.3 that a simply supported rectangular beam can only redistribute stresses across its depth at the most stressed section, but that a fixed beam, after redistributing stresses first across the depth of the most stressed section, proceeds to redistribute stresses across the depth of other less stressed sections. In a plate, peak stresses, that is, maximum **principal** stresses, occur only at one or at a few points, and most sections are understressed. As the load increases, the most stressed section redistributes stresses across its depth, while stresses increase at other sections. As soon as one of the sections yields and flows, the stresses at other sections increase up to the yield point and then flow progressively, until entire **lines of sections** may flow, thus creating **hinge lines** (Fig. 10.32). When the plate has developed enough hinge lines to become a moving mechanism, it cannot carry additional loads. Whereas redistribution of stress can take place in a beam at only one or a few sections before failure occurs, in a plate redistribution can take place along an entire line of sections. Hence, the reserve of strength is greater in a two-dimensional element like a plate than in a one-dimensional structure. The reserve of strength in a simply supported square plate under uniform load is 80 per cent as against 50 per cent in a simply supported beam.

In the discussion of stress redistribution in beams (see Section 9.3) it was implicitly assumed that the end sections of both simply supported and fixed beams are free to move **longitudinally,** so that the neutral beam axis **does not change length** [Fig. 10.33(a)]. When the end sections are restrained from moving longitudinally, the deflection of the beam under load requires a lengthening of the middle axis of the beam, and introduces tension in the beam [Fig. 10.33(b)]. When the beam material has tensile resistance, the

258

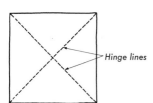

10.32 Hinge lines of square plate.

10.33 Cable action due to longitudinal restraint of beam ends.

longitudinal restraint of the end sections develops a certain amount of **cable action** in the beam, due to the tension along the curved beam axis. A beam with ends free to move carries loads exclusively by bending and shear, that is, by **beam action;** a longitudinally restrained beam carries loads partly by beam, and partly by cable action. An additional reserve of strength thus appears in the restrained beam; as the beam yields at some sections, and finally becomes a mechanism incapable of carrying additional load in bending, the sag of the middle axis increases and the additional load is carried by cable action. Such "cable action" cannot take place substantially in unrestrained beams, because they can deflect **without** stretching their middle axis.

A rectangular plate, simply supported along two **opposite** sides and free along the other two, behaves very much like a series of parallel beams; if its simply supported sides are free to move, the plate cannot develop cable stresses. Cable stresses will, instead, be developed if the two opposite sides are restrained from moving.

A square plate, simply supported on **all four** sides, deflects under a uniform load into a shape which requires a **stretch** of its middle surface, **even** if its sides are free to move (Fig. 10.15). Such shapes are called **nondevelopable,** because they cannot be "developed" or flattened into a plane without appropriate cuts. A sphere is a nondevelopable surface; it can be flattened without being stretched only if it is cut radially at a number of sections; a

260

cylinder, on the other hand, is a **developable** surface which can be flattened without cuts (see also Section 12.2).

The deflection surfaces of plates under loads are in almost all cases nondevelopable. Hence, the middle plane of the plate must stretch to acquire such deflections, and stresses are developed in the **middle plane** of the plate capable of carrying some load by **membrane action.** Membrane action is the two-dimensional equivalent of one-dimensional cable action; it is the action developed by a very thin sheet of a flexible material, such as cloth (see also Section 11.2).

In general, a plate develops membrane action as soon as it deflects under loads, and its load-carrying capacity is shared by plate action and membrane action. Membrane action develops even when the plate sides are free to move, but is substantially greater when the sides are restrained. Under growing loads, a plate first redistributes bending stresses at various sections until it becomes incapable of carrying any additional load by plate action. But, at the same time, the plate develops membrane action, and does not fail until the tensile membrane stresses reach the yield point. Inasmuch as the plate deflects into a nondevelopable surface because of its "two-dimensionality," the continuity of the plate material in two directions gives the plate an inherently greater reserve of strength.

10.7 Folded Plates

The structural efficiency of plates can be increased by stiffening them with ribs, thus removing some of the material from the neighborhood of the unstressed neutral plane of the plate. The same result may also be achieved by folding the plate. A sheet of paper, held along one side, cannot support its own weight, because its minute thickness does not give a sufficient lever arm to the bending stresses [Fig. 10.34(a)]. Folding the paper sheet brings the material of the cross section away from its "middle plane," and increases the lever arm of the bending stresses, which becomes comparable to the depth of the folded strips [Fig. 10.34(b)]. In fact, two plates at an angle are equivalent to a rectangular cross-section beam with a depth equal to the depth of the plates, and a width equal to the combined horizontal width of the two plates (Fig. 10.35).

Folded plates may be made of wood, steel, aluminum, or reinforced concrete. Reinforced-concrete folded plates are particularly economical because their formwork may be built of straight planks, or the concrete slabs may be prefabricated on the ground, lifted into place, and connected by welding the transverse bars at the folds, thus avoiding most of the formwork altogether.

(a)   (b)   **10.34** Folded plate.

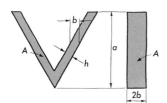

10.35 Rectangular beam equivalent to folded plate.

Folded-plate action is a combination of transverse and longitudinal beam action. Since their length is many times their width, the single slabs develop only one-dimensional beam action, in the direction of their width, that is, transversely (see Section 10.4). An ideal transverse strip of slab behaves like a continuous beam supported at the folds (Fig. 10.36). When the folded plate is supported on rigid end frames, the transverse supports offered by the folds are perfectly rigid in the neighborhood of the plate ends and flexible towards the middle of the span. The transverse strip on rigid or flexible supports develops reactions at the folds, which may be split into components (as in a triangular truss) loading the slabs in their own planes. These longitudinal reactions are carried to the end frames by the slabs acting as deep rectangular beams (Fig. 10.37). Thus, the load is transferred to the folds by beam action of the slabs in the transverse direction, and to the end frames by longitudinal beam action of the slabs.

264

(a)

(b)

10.36 Transverse continuous beam action in folded plates.

10.37 Longitudinal beam action in folded plates.

A uniformly loaded roof, consisting of a large number of folded plates, develops the same deflections in all the slabs, except those near its external boundary. The transverse strips of interior slabs move down by the same amount at each fold, and behave as continuous beams on **rigid** supports, since equal displacements of all the supports do not stress a continuous beam. The exterior slabs, instead, have differential displacements between the external and the internal fold supports, and carry more load by transverse bending than the interior slabs. Thus, each unit strip of an interior slab acts transversely as a fixed-end beam of unit width and depth h, and longitudinally as a rectangular beam of width b and depth a (Figs. 10.35 and 10.36). The exterior slabs require a more detailed analysis and are more highly stressed than the interior slabs. To avoid overstressing, the exterior slabs may be stiffened by additional vertical, deep beams at the boundary; the one-sided lack of support of the exterior slabs is thus compensated for by the supporting action of the boundary beams (Fig. 10.38).

Folded plates may be given a variety of cross-sectional shapes. Some of the commonly used arrangements are shown in Fig. 10.38.

The increase in stiffness due to folding may be extended to other than longitudinal folds. Polygonal and circular folded plates may be used to cover circular areas; in this case the plates are given a rise at the center, where the depth of the slabs peters out [Fig. 10.39(a)]. Each radial element of the folded plate behaves like a truss or arch; it develops a thrust, usually absorbed by a circumferential tie-rod, and may be considered hinged at the crown, since the small depth available there makes impossible the development of bending stresses [Fig. 10.39(b)].

266

10.38 Folded-plate cross sections.

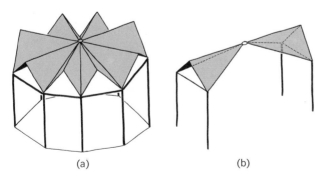

(a)   (b)

10.39 Polygonal folded plates.

10.40 Folded-plate construction.

Folded plates are used mainly as roof structures, but their application to floors becomes practical whenever their depth can be used to house mechanical systems. Folded plates may also be used as vertical walls to resist both vertical and horizontal loads. Combinations of folded-plate walls and roofs have been used to enclose large spaces (Fig. 10.40). The reader may wish to experiment with this type of construction by folding a sheet of paper along the lines indicated in Fig. 10.41 and taping it to a piece of cardboard. The barrel-type structure thus obtained is capable of supporting very substantial loads, although the paper may be only one one-hundredth of an inch thick (Fig. 10.42). The creased-paper structure collapses if its boundary is allowed to move. The collapse is due mostly to buckling of the thin slabs in those areas where compression is developed.

268

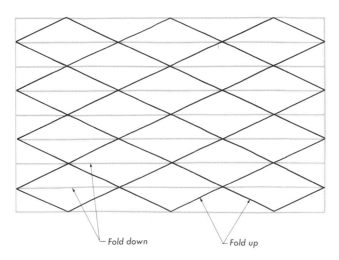

Fold down   Fold up

10.41 Creased-paper barrel folds.

10.42 Creased-paper barrel.

Chapter Eleven

Membranes

11.1 Membranes

A membrane is a sheet of material so thin that, to all practical purposes, it cannot resist compression, bending, or shear, but only tension. A piece of cloth or a sheet of rubber is a good example of a membrane. Soap bubbles are extremely thin membranes; they can span plane or skew boundaries; their most remarkable property is to have the minimum area among all surfaces with a given boundary (Fig. 11.1). By the same token, they are also the smoothest surfaces among those with that boundary.

Not withstanding their weakness in relation to most states of stress, human ingenuity has found ways and means of using membranes for structural purposes, mainly because of their lightness. The circus tent is a membrane capable of spanning hundreds of feet, provided its cloth is properly supported by compressive struts, stabilized by tensioned guy wires (Fig. 11.2). The tent withstands the pressure of the wind, but even under ideal circumstances presents the drawback of moving under variable loads: a membrane adapts its shape to carry loads by tension, and behaves like a two-dimensional **funicular surface.** Moreover, because of its light weight, the tent vibrates or "flutters" under the action of a variable, or even a steady, wind. Tents are useful as temporary covers, but unacceptable as permanent roofs.

11.1 Minimal membrane.

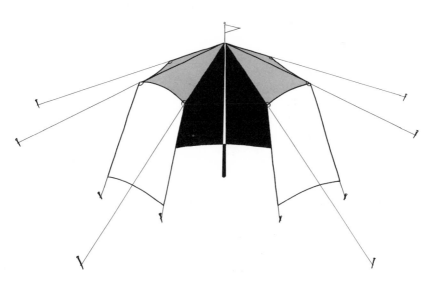

11.2 Circus tent.

The structural action of a membrane is greatly improved by tensioning it before it is loaded. Firemen use a round sheet of cloth, tensioned on an outer ring, to catch people jumping from great heights. The thin sheet takes the impact of the falling person, deflects elastically, and saves the jumper by its flexibility and strength. The combination of sheet and ring, even though unloaded, has "locked-in" stresses of the type described in Section 2.5. Firemen's membranes are typical prestressed elements. The tension in the sheet and the compression in the ring are produced by the radial pull of the rope connecting the sheet to the ring.

The umbrella is another example of a prestressed membrane with locked-in stresses. The curved steel ribs, pushed out and supported by the compressive struts connected to the stick, tension the cloth, and give it a shape suited to carrying loads. Within limits, the membrane of an umbrella can take pressures from above and from below: the supporting steel skeleton reverses its stresses with the reversal of wind action, but the membrane is under tension in both cases (Fig. 11.3).

The Eskimo kayak is built by means of a membrane of seal skins tensioned by a skeleton of longitudinal bars and circumferential rings pushed into it. A modern version of a kayak is built by means of a membrane of rubberized cloth, stretched by an internal frame. Such is the strength of these little boats that they have been sailed across the Atlantic by solitary navigators, although only 17 feet long and 3 feet wide.

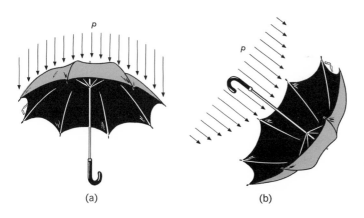

(a)   (b)

11.3 Prestressed membrane of an umbrella.

Interesting roof shapes can be created by prestressed membranes. Figure 11.4 shows a tent in the form of a saddle, designed by Frei Otto, in which the tension of the ropes anchored to the ground stabilizes the tent suspended from two poles. Figure 11.5 illustrates a circular tent roof, designed by Horacio Caminos, in which a circular cloth attached to a compression ring is tensioned by the action of compressive struts. Pretensioned membranes are stiffer and more stable than unstressed membranes; they do not flutter or move as easily under variable loads.

The prestressing of the hull of the Zeppelin dirigibles was obtained by two separate methods; an internal skeleton supported the membrane, which was tensioned by the pressure of hydrogen. The rigidity obtained by this combination allowed the hull to take the severe dynamic loads imposed by air pockets and turbulence.

Membranes can be prestressed by internal pressure alone when they completely enclose a volume, or a number of separate volumes. They constitute **pneumatic structures.** Membrane structures consisting of an enclosed volume are used, for example, in rubber rafts: the outer inflated ring is stiff enough to be used as a compression ring for the unstressed membrane forming the bottom of the raft. An inflatable airplane has been built on the same principle, with inflated wings and an inflated fuselage divided into separate compartments; it was flown by a light engine.

276

11.4 Membrane tent.

11.5 Prestressed circular roof.

Plastic membranes covering swimming pools or other temporary installations may be blown up by a small pressure to create stable domes (Fig. 11.6). An overpressure of only one or two tenths of a pound per square inch is sufficient to hold up such structures, which can be entered through regular doors, since the loss of pressure in the large enclosed volume is negligible even if the door is opened frequently; such losses as do occur are replaced intermittently under control of a pressure gage. Large spherical domes over radar installations (radomes) are built on the same principle by means of extremely thin plastic membranes, which do not interfere with the reception and transmission of electromagnetic beams. Radomes are built up to diameters of 150 feet.

Figure 11.7 illustrates the balloon roof of a summer theater designed by Carl Koch and Paul Weidlinger. The balloon, in the form of a lens, spans 150 feet and is inflated by a pump to an overpressure of 10 pounds per square foot. The balloon has a circular opening at the top, and new air is continuously pumped into it to reduce overheating and the consequent variations in air pressure and changes in shape of the balloon. The roof can be lifted to the top of its supporting steel ring and inflated in less than 20 minutes. Its shape is insensitive to steady winds; the balloon does not tend to fly away. The inflated balloon is to be used, for the last time, as formwork for a concrete dome to be sprayed over it.

Balloon forms for concrete were used in the construction of the so-called "igloo houses," invented by Neff and designed by Noyes and Salvadori (Fig. 11.8). The inflated balloon supports a reinforcing steel mesh, over which a layer of one inch of concrete is sprayed by a concrete gun. Once the concrete has hardened, the form is deflated and pulled out of the house through the door opening.

278

Swimming pool

11.6 Pneumatic roof.

11.7 Balloon roof.

(a)

(b)

11.8 Igloo (balloon) houses.

The long plastic balloons used at children's parties become so stiff when inflated, that they can develop compression and bending action. The internal pressure locks into the cylindrical balloons tensile stresses in the circumferential and in the longitudinal directions. (The circumferential stress is often referred to as the "hoop stress" by analogy with the tensile stresses locked into the hoops of a barrel.) The inflated cylinder supports compressive loads, as a column, up to the point where the compression due to the load equals the longitudinal tension due to the internal pressure. When the compression nears this value, the membrane buckles.

Similarly, a balloon used as a horizontal beam carries loads up to the point where the compressive stresses in the upper fibers of the beam equal the tensile stresses produced by the internal pressure. The reader may easily prove that when the compressive stress nears this value, the beam buckles at the top.

Although pneumatic elements so far have seldom been used in architectural structures, it is conceivable that they might soon become popular, because of the availability of thin plastic membranes with exceptionally high tensile resistance.

Membrane roofs have been built not only of cloth, but of steel, aluminum, and reinforced concrete. Metal membranes are well adapted to carrying loads by tensile stresses, but seldom present an economical solution to the roof problem. Reinforced concrete may be so reinforced or prestressed as to make it suitable to the development of tensile stresses. The Viera circular roof may be considered a concrete prestressed membrane (see Fig. 6.27); the cable-supported roof of the Nowicki arena may be considered a cable-supported membrane made up of metal sheet elements (see Fig. 6.24). It was indicated in Section 6.4 that light metal structures have a tendency to flutter, while the heavier concrete membranes do not. Thus, the thickness of a structural membrane may be increased for other than strength reasons, and the membrane may acquire some of the characteristics of a plate. Just as plates are bound to develop some membrane action in deflecting under applied loads (see Section 10.6), membranes are bound to develop some plate action due to their finite thickness. In view of the greater efficiency of membrane action (Section 11.2), the thickness of a membrane should be kept minimal, provided its shape and displacements are functionally acceptable.

11.2 Membrane Stresses

Although a membrane is a two-dimensional resisting structure, it does not develop appreciable plate stresses (bending and shear) because its depth is very small in comparison with its span (see Section 10.6). Therefore, the load-carrying capacity of membranes must come from other types of stresses.

It was noted in Section 6.1 that a cable can support loads in tension because it sags, and that it is structurally efficient because its tensile stresses are distributed uniformly across its sections. A membrane supports loads by a similar mechanism and presents the same kind of structural efficiency.

Figure 11.9 shows an element cut out of a curved membrane and acted upon by a **normal** load. Since the sag of the element produces in the membrane curvatures in two directions, the membrane may be considered, at first, as the intersection of two cables; each cable carries a share of the load, and the total load carried by the membrane is the sum of the two "cable" loads Thus, a membrane is seen to be capable of "cable action in two directions."

The two-dimensional resisting character of a membrane makes it also capable of a second load-carrying mechanism through the development of shears acting **within** the membrane surface, **provided the membrane is not buckled by the equivalent diagonal compression.** One may prove that a thin piece of material can develop such shears by holding a **vertical** sheet of paper along one of its edges and by pulling **vertically** along its opposite edge (Fig. 11.10). The paper sheet carries the load **acting in its own plane** by **tangential** shears. But, just as the tension in a horizontal cable cannot carry vertical loads, the shears in the plane of the paper sheet cannot, by themselves, carry loads perpendicular to it. The load-carrying action of a membrane is due to its **curved** shape.

Figure 11.11 shows a rectangular element cut out of a curved membrane, and indicates that, in general, its four sides are not parallel, but askew in space; this means that one of its sides slopes more than the opposite side, and that a **difference** in slope occurs between these two sides. The figure also shows that a difference in slope between two opposite sides necessarily requires a difference in slope between the **other** two opposite sides. The dif-

282

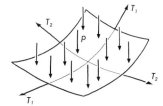

11.9 Cable loads in membrane.

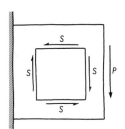

11.10 Shear development in plane of membrane.

11.11 Membrane twist.

ference in slope between opposite sides is called the **twist** of the membrane surface. Since the slope of a membrane surface in a given direction usually changes from point to point, membranes, in general, have both curvatures and twist. The curvatures and the twist characterize the geometrical behavior of the membrane surface at a given point.

The two pairs of shears on the sides of any membrane element have directions that guarantee equilibrium in rotation (see Section 5.3), as shown in Fig. 11.10; but in a twisted membrane the difference in slope between two opposite shears produces an **excess** of normal upward forces (Fig. 11.12). It is this excess that balances part of the normal load and gives the membrane its load-carrying capacity by shearing action within its own surface.

Membranes that do not buckle are thus seen to carry normal load by three separate mechanisms: cable action due to curvature in one direction; cable action due to curvature at right angles to the first; and shear action due to twist. Any one of these three actions vanishes if the corresponding curvature, or the twist, vanishes.

284

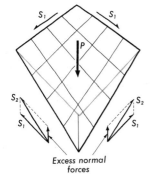

Excess normal
forces

11.12 Portion of normal load carried by shears.

11.3 Principal Curvatures and Principal Stresses in Membranes

The results obtained in the preceding section indicate the two essential characteristics of membrane action. **Membrane stresses,** both tensile and shearing, are always developed in the membrane surface and never at right angles to it. Membrane action depends essentially on the geometrical characteristics of the membrane shape, that is, on its curvature and its twist.

In order to visualize the curvatures of a membrane surface, one cuts the surface with a plane perpendicular to it. Figure 11.13 shows that, for a cylinder, a perpendicular plane parallel to the axis cuts the cylinder along a straight line, indicating a lack of curvature in this direction. A cut at right angles to the axis has, instead, a substantial curvature, while cuts in any other direction show **smaller** curvatures. It is thus seen that as the cutting plane rotates around the normal to the cylinder, the sections acquire curvatures that vary from zero in one direction to a maximum value at right angles to it. The two directions in which the curvatures become respectively maximum and minimum (in the present example the minimum is zero) are called the **principal directions of curvature** of the membrane. For an element of the cylinder with sides parallel to these directions it is seen that the element has **no twist** [Fig. 11.14(a)]. But an element cut out of the cylinder with sides not parallel to the principal directions has twist [Fig. 11.14(b)]. Thus a surface may have twist in certain directions and no twist in others. The only surface without twist in any direction is the sphere, since an element cut by any two pairs of parallel sides is identical to an element cut by **any other** two pairs of sides.

The properties exhibited by the cylinder in relation to curvature and twist are not peculiar to this surface, but completely general. **Any surface** cut by planes passing through its normal at a point exhibits two directions at right

11.13 Cylinder curvatures.

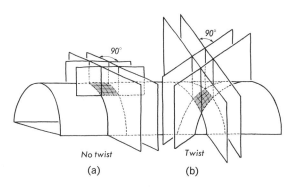

No twist   Twist

(a)   (b)

11.14 Cylinder twist.

angles to each other for which the curvature becomes, respectively, maximum and minimum; for these two perpendicular directions the surface has no twist. It is often convenient to spot principal curvature directions by the lack of twist —that is, of slope change—in these directions.

One may mark by means of small crosses the directions of principal curvature on a membrane surface, as was done for the case of principal stresses, and obtain a pattern of **lines of principal curvature.** For a cylinder this pattern is a rectangular mesh with sides parallel to the axis and at right angles to it. Figure 11.15 indicates the principal curvature lines for a general surface.

The membrane stresses at a point of a membrane have different values in different directions, just like the beam stresses considered in Section 9.2. Hence, as the orientation of the stress rotates around a point, the stress becomes maximum and minimum in two directions at right angles, the **directions of principal stress.** Elements oriented in these directions do not develop shear; shear becomes greatest at 45 degrees to the directions of principal stress.

The directions of principal stress are those in which the membrane acts as two sets of cables at right angles; one set develops the maximum stress, the other set the minimum stress at each point. Indicating by small crosses the directions of principal stress at a number of points, one may obtain a pattern of **principal stress lines** for the membrane. Whereas the lines of principal curvature are a geometrical characteristic of the membrane surface, the lines of principal stress depend on the shape of the surface, the character of the load, and the conditions of support [Fig. 11.16(a)]. In certain cases of symmetry, the two patterns may exceptionally coincide, as for a sphere or a cylinder under internal pressure [Fig. 11.16(b)].

288

11.15 Principal curvature lines.

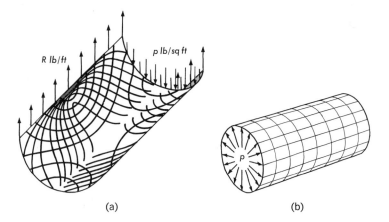

$R \ lb/ft$ $p \ lb/sq \ ft$

(a)   (b)

11.16 Principal stress lines of cylindrical membranes (a) under dead load, (b) under internal pressure.

The analysis of cable action showed that the stresses developed in a cable are inversely proportional to its span-to-sag ratio (see Section 6.1). Conversely, **for a given allowable stress,** the greater the sag, the greater the load the cable can safely carry. Considering the cable action of a membrane along its principal stress directions, it is thus found that the direction with greater sag ratio—that is, greater curvature—carries more load than the direction with smaller sag ratio (smaller curvature). In the case of a sphere, the curvature is the same in all directions, and a spherical membrane under uniform pressure carries half of it by cable action in one direction and half of it by cable action in the other. In the case of a cylinder under uniform normal pressure, the straight lines carry no load, since they have no curvature, and the entire load is carried by stresses along the curvature lines at right angles to the cylinder axis. The stresses developed by this cable action are the hoop stresses referred to in Section 11.1.

Since buckling stresses are proportional to the square of the thickness-to-span ratio, membranes buckle under extremely low compressive stresses. It is thus correct to say that, **to all practical purposes,** membranes cannot develop compressive stresses. By the same token, the membrane shears developed by a membrane are also negligible, because shears produce an equivalent 45-degree compression.

290

Since actual membranes cannot develop compression or shear, they carry load **by tension only,** and act essentially as a **network of cables.** When the load changes, the shape of the membrane also changes and adapts the curvatures to the values needed to carry the new load. Membranes, like cables, are unstable; they must be stabilized by the action of an inner skeleton, by the tension produced by external forces, or by internal pressure. Prestressing by tensioning allows the membrane to develop compressive stresses up to values capable of canceling the tensile stresses locked in the membrane; it adds to the advantage of aerodynamic stability that of carrying loads by the shear mechanism.

It must be noted that the stresses in a membrane, being almost totally tensile, are uniformly distributed across its thickness; the utilization of the material in membranes is optimal. Moreover, tensile strains are always small compared to bending strains, so that the membrane deflections due to loads are usually small. (These deflections should not be confused with the **displacements** of the membrane due to **variations** in the load, which may be quite large.) Thus, by the nature of their load-carrying action membranes are light, economical, and stiff under steady loads. As noted above, their use in permanent structures has been limited exclusively by their mobility.

Chapter Twelve

Thin Shells

12.1 Form-resistant Structures

A sheet of paper held in the hand bends limply and cannot support its own weight. The same sheet of paper, if pinched and given a slight upward curvature, is capable of supporting its own weight and some additional load (Fig. 12.1). The new carrying capacity is obtained not by increasing the amount of material used, but by giving it proper form. The upward curvature increases the stiffness and the load-carrying capacity of the paper sheet because it locates some material away from the "neutral axis," so that the bending rigidity of the sheet, considered as a beam, is substantially increased. The same result is achieved by creasing the paper, that is, by giving it sudden changes in slope or **concentrated curvatures** (see Section 10.7).

Structures in which strength is obtained by shaping the material according to the loads they must carry are called **form-resistant structures.** Membranes (see Chapter 11) depend on curvature to carry loads; they belong to the category of form-resistant structures in which the shape allows loads to be carried in tension. A membrane turned upside down, and carrying the same loads for which it was originally shaped, would be a form-resistant structure developing only compression—that is, the **two-dimensional antifunicular** for those loads (see Section 6.1).

Their mobility and their incapacity to resist compressive or shear stresses restricts the use of membranes (see Section 11.2). All the disadvantages of membrane action are avoided—and most advantages are maintained—in

294

12.1 Form-resistant structure.

thin shells. Thin shells are form-resistant structures thin enough not to develop appreciable bending stresses, but thick enough to carry loads by compression, shear, and tension. Although thin shells have been built of wood, steel, and plastic materials, they are ideally suited to reinforced-concrete construction. Thin shells allow the economical construction of domes and other curved roofs of varied form, great beauty, and exceptional strength. They are among the most sophisticated expressions of modern structural design.

Thin shells owe their efficiency to curvatures and twist. In order to understand their structural action one must first become familiar with their purely geometrical characteristics.

12.2 Curvatures

It was seen in Section 11.2 that the curvature of a surface at a point is exhibited by cutting it with planes pivoted around the normal to the surface at that point. The curvature varies as the plane rotates; it may be up or down in all directions, or up in some and down in others. Moreover, a surface has, in general, a twist, since its slope changes as one moves at right angles to the direction of the slope.

All the intersections of a dome with a plane passing through its normal have **downward** curvatures. For spherical domes the curvatures are all identical (Fig. 12.2); for any other type of dome, they change from a maximum to a minimum as the plane rotates (Fig. 12.3). On the other hand, the curvatures

296

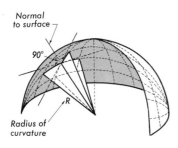

12.2 Curvatures of spherical dome.

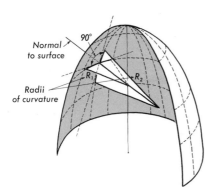

12.3 Curvatures of dome.

of a teacup are all up. Surfaces like domes or cups, in which the curvature changes value around a point but is always up or down, are called **synclastic** (from the Greek words **syn** = with, and **klastos** = to cut). It is convenient to call downward curvatures positive, and upward curvatures negative; with this convention, domes have positive curvatures and cups negative curvatures in all directions. Surfaces with positive or negative curvature at all points are said to be **nondevelopable,** because they cannot be flattened unless they are cut at a number of sections (Fig. 12.4). Their stiffness and strength stems, in large part, from their resistance to those deformations which tend to flatten them, that is, to reduce their curvatures.

As the curvature in a given direction becomes smaller, the surface approaches the shape of a cylinder. The curvature in the direction of the cylinder axis, one of the principal curvatures (see Fig. 11.14), is zero. Surfaces, like those of barrel roofs or gutter channels, with curvatures always positive or always negative, but vanishing in one direction, are called **developable** surfaces; they can be flattened without introducing cuts. Developable surfaces are obviously less stiff and strong than synclastic surfaces.

298

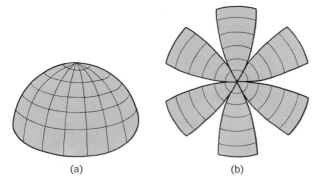

(a)　　　　　　　　　　(b)

12.4 Development of a synclastic surface.

A horse saddle has a downward curvature "across the horse" and an upward curvature "along the horse": as one cuts the saddle with a vertical rotating plane its curvature changes not only in value, but also in sign; a mountain pass presents the same behavior (Fig. 12.5). As the cutting plane rotates around its axis, the curvature of the saddle changes **gradually** from positive to negative values, and back to positive values again; therefore, the curvature must **vanish** in two directions. Saddle surfaces have, in general, two directions of zero curvature—that is, two directions along which two straight lines lie **on** the surface (Fig. 12.5); they are also nondevelopable. The lines of principal curvature of a saddle surface are shown in Fig. 12.6. One may talk of the "top of the dome," or even the "top of the cylinder," which is a ridge of tops, but one cannot really define the top of a saddle surface. The "top of the mountain pass" is a real top for those coming from the valley, but a "bottom" for those coming down the ridges of the adjoining mountains.

Surfaces exhibiting zero curvature in **more** than two directions at a point are easily constructed. A surface with no curvature in three directions is called a **monkey saddle,** since a monkey can straddle it with its legs, and have its tail down on it (Fig. 12.7). A surface with more than three lines of zero curvature has a scalloped shape.

300

12.5 Saddle surface.

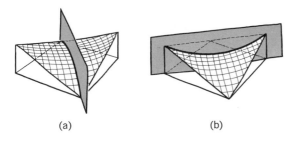

(a) (b)

12.6 Principal curvature lines of saddle surface.

12.7 The monkey saddle.

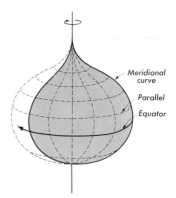

Meridional curve

Parallel

Equator

12.8 Rotational surface.

12.3 Rotational Surfaces

Shell surfaces were classified in Section 12.2 according to their curvatures at a point. A different classification, depending on their general shape, is also of great significance in shell design, and will be used in later sections to analyze the over-all behavior of the most commonly encountered shell roofs.

Rotational surfaces are described by the rotation of a plane curve around a vertical axis (Fig. 12.8). The plane or **meridional curve** may have a variety of shapes, thus giving rise to a variety of dome forms, well suited to the roofing of a circular area. The most commonly used dome is **spherical:** its surface is obtained by rotating an arc of circle around a vertical axis. The vertical sections of a rotational shell are called its **meridians** and its horizontal sections, which are all circles, its **parallels;** the largest parallel is called the **equator**.

Complete spheres, supported on a ring or on stilts, are often used as metal tanks for liquid chemicals (Fig. 12.9). Liquid containers are also built as rotational surfaces in the shape of a drop of water. Since a drop of water is kept together by the constant capillary tension of its surface, these containers are designed to develop a constant tension, and are most efficient in storing liquids.

Elliptical domes are described by half an ellipse rotating around its vertical axis [Fig. 12.10(a)]; their action is not as efficient as the action of a spherical dome because the top of the shell is flatter, and the reduction in curvature introduces larger stresses. On the other hand, the parabolic dome [Fig. 12.10(b)] may have a sharper curvature at its top and present structural advantages even in comparison with the sphere.

302

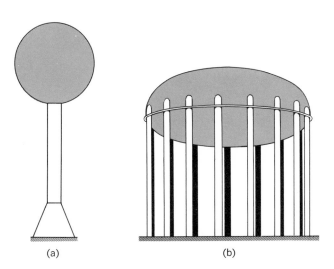

(a)　　　　　(b)

12.9 Liquid shell-tanks.

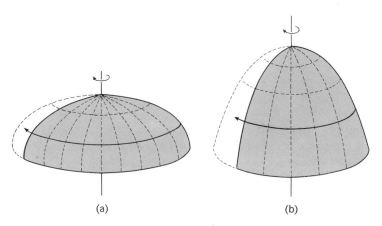

(a)　　　　　(b)

12.10 Elliptical and parabolic surfaces of revolution.

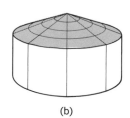

(a)   (b)

12.11 Conical surfaces.

The surface described by rotating a straight line around a vertical axis is a **cone.** Conical surfaces are commonly used as umbrellas, when supported at a point, and as domes when supported on their circular boundary (Fig. 12.11). The lack of curvature in the radial direction of the cone makes the forming of cones in reinforced concrete somewhat simpler than the forming of regular domes.

Circular curved barrels are obtained by rotating around a vertical axis a half-circle or any other curve **not intersecting the axis;** such surfaces are called **toruses,** and are well suited to roof ring areas (Fig. 12.12).

12.4 Translational Surfaces

The surface of a **translational shell** is obtained by "translating," that is, sliding a plane curve on another plane curve, usually at right angles to the first. A cylinder is obtained by translating a horizontal straight line along a vertical curve, or translating a vertical curve along a horizontal straight line, perpendicular to it; depending on the curve, the cylinder may be circular, parabolic, or elliptic (Fig. 12.13). When the straight line is inclined, the cylinder also becomes inclined, and is well suited to roof a staircase by means of a barrel-like vault.

304

12.12 Torus surface.

(a)

(b)

12.13 Cylindrical surfaces.

The translation of a vertical parabola with downward curvature on a perpendicular parabola with downward curvature generates a surface called an **elliptic paraboloid,** which covers a rectangular area; its horizontal sections are ellipses; its vertical sections are parabolas (Fig. 12.14). When the two parabolas are identical, the paraboloid covers a square area, and its horizontal sections become circles. The elliptic paraboloid was the first shape ever used to build a thin shell.

A **hyperbolic paraboloid (hypar** for short, in Great Britain) is obtained by translating a parabola with downward curvature on a parabola with upward curvature [Fig. 12.15(a)]. This surface has the appearance of a saddle; its horizontal sections are two separate branches of a curve called a hyperbola, while its vertical principal sections are parabolas [Fig. 12.15(b)]. As for all other saddle surfaces, the curvatures of the hyperbolic paraboloid vanish in two directions. But, for a hyperbolic paraboloid these directions are the **same at all points.** This means that the vertical sections parallel to these directions are **all straight lines,** called generatrices, and that the hyperbolic paraboloid has a **double** set of straight lines **lying on its surface.** Hence, this surface may

306

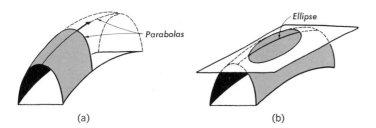

(a)　　　　　　　　　(b)

12.14 Elliptic paraboloid.

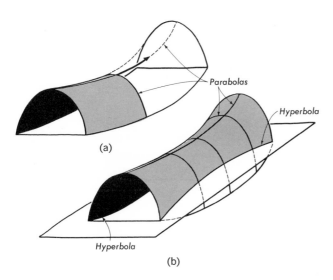

(a)

(b)

12.15 Hyperbolic paraboloid.

also be generated by a straight-line segment sliding with its two ends on two straight lines askew in space (Fig. 12.16). The forming of such a surface in reinforced concrete is relatively simple, since it involves the use of straight planks in the direction of the lines of zero curvature.

When the two curves used in translation are not at right angles to each other, the translational surface covers a skewed rectangle.

A great variety of surfaces can be obtained by translation, since **any** curve may be translated on **any other** curve for this purpose, but not all translational surfaces are well suited to carry loads.

12.5 Ruled Surfaces

The hyperbolic paraboloid was shown in Section 12.4 to have a double set of straight lines lying on its surface. Any surface generated by sliding the two ends of a straight-line segment on two separate curves is called a **ruled surface.** When the two curves are two straight lines askew in space, the ruled surface is a hyperbolic paraboloid (Fig. 12.16). The cylinder is a ruled surface generated by sliding a horizontal line segment on two **identical** vertical curves [Fig. 12.13(a)].

A different family of ruled surfaces is obtained by sliding a straight-line segment on two **different** curves lying in **parallel** planes; these are called **conoidal** surfaces. Conoidal roofs cover a rectangular area and allow light to enter from a given direction, usually from the north (Fig. 12.17).

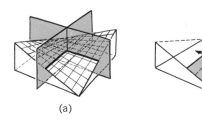

(a)   (b)

12.16 Straight-line generatrices of hyperbolic paraboloid.

12.17 Conoidal surface.

12.18 Conoid.

Conoids are conoidal surfaces obtained by sliding a segment with one of its ends on a **curve** and the other on a **straight line** (Fig. 12.18). The conoid is called circular, parabolic, or elliptic depending on whether its end curve is an arc of a circle, a parabola, or an ellipse. The conoid is a saddle surface; its principal-curvature lines show that the curvature in the direction of the lines connecting the top of the curve to the opposite corners is upward, while the transverse curvature is downward (Fig. 12.18). Conoids may be used as cantilevered shells with their curved end at the root of the cantilever; in this case their transverse curvature is usually directed upward (Fig. 12.19).

Cones are ruled surfaces in which one end of the segment rotates about a point and the other slides on a curve. **Conical sectors** are conoidal surfaces and may be used to cover trapezoidal areas, or as cantilevered roofs, much as conoids are (Fig. 12.20).

An inclined segment sliding on two horizontal circles describes a surface called a **hyperboloid of one sheet,** whose vertical sections are two-branch hyperbolas (Fig. 12.21). These easily formed surfaces are extensively used to build cooling towers in cement plants and in other industrial plants.

12.19 Cantilevered conoid.

12.20 Conical sector.

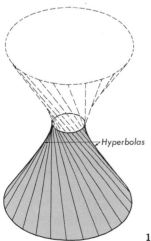

Hyperbolas

12.21 Hyperboloid of one sheet.

12.22 Intersecting cylinders.

12.23 Undulated cylindrical surface.

12.6 Complex Surfaces

The elementary, geometrically defined surfaces of the previous section may be combined in any number of ways to obtain more complex surfaces. Two cylindrical shells may be intersected at right angles to cover a square or a rectangular area (Fig. 12.22). Parallel cylinders with curvatures alternately upward and downward create an undulated roof similar to a folded plate (Fig. 12.23). Scalloped ringed roofs may be obtained by joining sectors of cones with curvature alternately upward and downward (Fig. 12.24). Moreover, any of the elementary forms may be scalloped to obtain more playful and, at times, more efficient structural shells. An ellipsoid may be scalloped to give it curvature towards the supported edge (Fig. 12.25). A parabolic cylinder may be undulated to transform it into a surface with curvatures in two directions rather than in one, thus stiffening it (Fig. 12.26). Spherical domes may be undulated for the same purpose (Fig. 12.27).

312

12.24 Undulated conical surface.

12.25 Scalloped ellipsoid.

12.26 Undulated parabolic cylinder.

12.27 Undulated spherical sector.

12.28 Hyperbolic paraboloid combination.

12.29 Hyperbolic paraboloidal conoid.

Hyperbolic paraboloids may be used in a variety of combinations. Four identical paraboloids form a corner-supported roof covering a rectangular area, one of the most commonly used combinations of this surface (Fig. 12.28). Two hyperbolic paraboloids may be combined to form a north-light conoidal roof (Fig. 12.29) or a cantilevered shell (Fig. 12.30). Four paraboloids supported on a central column form an umbrella roof (Fig. 12.31). When the angle between the two planes of its two translating parabolas is not a right angle, the hyperbolic paraboloid is called **skew,** and may be used to cover nonrectangular areas (Fig. 12.32).

314

12.30 Cantilevered hyperbolic paraboloidal conoid.

12.31 Hyperbolic paraboloid umbrella.

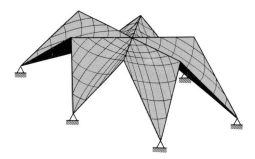

12.32 Skew hyperbolic paraboloid combination.

There is no reason to limit the shape of a thin shell to forms easily definable by geometrical formulas. Structurally sound, "free" shapes may be invented. But the imagination of the designer becomes mere fancy unless he is familiar with the structural behavior of the basic geometric forms. Thin shells are extraordinarily efficient **structural** elements, and their shapes should be dictated primarily by structural considerations. The behavior under load of the most commonly used thin-shell forms must be considered first in terms of their **membrane action,** following the basic ideas presented in Chapter 11. More refined considerations of stress, as well as additional practical requirements, will be taken up in some detail in later sections.

12.7 **Membrane Action in Circular Domes**

The structural action of a rotational, or circular, dome under vertical loads **symmetrical** with respect to its axis (as the dead load) is a consequence of its geometrical characteristics. The meridional sections and the sections at right angles to the meridians are the principal curvature **and** principal stress sections (see Section 11.3). The stresses on these sections are simple tension or simple compression evenly distributed across their small thickness.

Figure 12.33 shows the stresses developed at a parallel; they are **compressive** stresses **in** the direction of the meridian and constant **along** the parallel, because the dome and the loads are symmetrical about the axis. Each meridian behaves as if it were a funicular arch for the applied loads, that is, it carries the loads without developing bending stresses.

316

12.33 Meridional stresses in spherical dome.

Arches were shown in Section 6.3 to be funicular for **only one set** of loads. The meridians of a dome, instead, are funicular for **any set** of symmetrical loads. This essential difference in structural behavior is due to the fact that while isolated arches have no lateral support, the meridians of the dome are **supported by the parallels,** which restrain their lateral displacement by developing hoop stresses. The contribution of the parallels to the funicular behavior of the dome is indicated by the deformations of the meridians under load. In a shallow or small-rise dome the meridians deflect under load, and in so doing move **inward,** that is, towards the dome axis (Fig. 12.34). In the two-dimensional structural dome this motion is accompanied by a **shortening** of the parallels, whose radius decreases. The parallels are compressed, and their resistance reduces substantially the freedom of the meridians to move inward. In other words, a shallow dome may be considered to act as a series of meridional arches elastically supported by the parallels. It develops compressive stresses along both the meridians and the parallels and, theoretically at least, can be built of materials incapable of developing tensile stresses, such as masonry or bricks.

When the dome has a high rise, the points of its top portion move inward under the action of the loads, but the points of its lower portion move outward, that is, **away** from the axis (Fig. 12.35). The parallels of the lower

318

12.34 Deformation of shallow spherical dome.

12.35 Deformation of high rise dome under dead load.

portion lengthen and develop tensile stresses, which again restrain this motion. Depending upon the type of load, one specific parallel remains unchanged in length, while all those above develop compression, and all those below develop tension. In a spherical dome under dead load the parallel at an angle of 52 degrees from the axis does not change length (Fig. 12.35). Under a snow load, uniformly distributed on the horizontal projection of the dome, the unstressed parallel is at 45 degrees to the axis. Whatever its rise, an arch acted upon by symmetrical loads tends to open up, and to thrust outward. Thus the action of a dome differs substantially from that of an arch; depending upon its rise, it pushes out or pulls in along its boundary.

Since the stresses developed by a dome are purely compressive and tensile, and the corresponding strains are very small (see Sections 5.1 and 5.2), the stiffness of circular domes is exceptionally high. The top of a concrete dome in the shape of a half sphere, 100 feet in diameter and only 3 inches thick, acted upon by a very heavy load of snow and its own dead load, deflects less than one tenth of an inch. The ratio of span to deflection is twelve thousand, and should be compared with an acceptable ratio of between 300 and 800 for a bending structure, such as a beam. The outward displacement of the dome at its boundary is even smaller than its vertical deflection: only three one-hundredths of an inch; the rotation of the boundary—that is, the change in direction of the meridians—is only 0.01 degrees (Fig. 12.34). A similar behavior is exhibited by rotational shells having other meridional sections.

The stiffness of circular domes explains why their thickness may be reduced to such small values; ratios of span-to-thickness of the order of 300 or more are customary. For example, a reinforced-concrete dome spanning 100 feet with a thickness of 3 inches has a ratio of span-to-thickness of 400. The steel domes used as containment spheres in nuclear reactors have ratios of the order of one thousand. Such ratios may be compared with the ratio of span-to-thickness in an eggshell, which is only 30, or in bending structures, which is of the order of 20.

As a consequence of its funicular behavior under **any** set of **symmetrical** loads, a dome does not change shape to adapt itself to a change in loads; therefore, it is a stable structure for such loads. It will now be seen that a dome is stable under any set of loads, symmetrical or unsymmetrical.

It was shown in Section 11.1 that membranes must change shape under varying loads, because they can develop only tensile stresses. In a thin dome, instead, if direct stresses along the meridians and the parallels cannot carry the entire load, a third mechanism is available to equilibrate the unbalanced difference: the shear mechanism considered in Section 11.2. Provided safe stresses are not exceeded, direct stresses (compression and tension) on one hand, and shear on the other, will always share and equilibrate the total load on a spherical dome element without requiring a change in its shape (Fig. 12.36). Taking into account the shear mechanism, a dome may be said to be funicular for **all** loads and, hence, to be a **stable structure** under any circumstances. For example, a dome resists lateral loads, such as wind pressures and suctions, by developing all three types of membrane stresses. The shear stresses due to wind are also of modest intensity: a 100 mile-an-hour wind on a dome 3 inches thick spanning 100 feet produces membrane shears of only 14 pounds per square inch.

12.8 Bending Stresses in Domes

A dome was shown to carry loads essentially by **membrane stresses** (compression, tension, and shear), because the development of shears makes it funicular for **all** loads. On the other hand, because it is so thin, if there were anywhere in the dome a tendency to develop bending stresses, these could easily exceed allowable values. It is therefore necessary to investigate the possibility of such a tendency.

In the analysis of the carrying capacity of thin domes it was tacitly assumed that domes are free to develop the minute displacements required by their membrane state of stress. Thus, the dome considered in Section 12.7 develops membrane stresses under load, and the corresponding strains give its top a small vertical displacement. Since this deflection is not prevented, a pure state of membrane stress exists in its neighborhood. An entirely different situation may develop, instead, at the boundary of the shell.

A spherical dome with a high rise tends to open up at the equator; its boundary displaces outward, even though by a very small amount. Moreover, the reactions supporting the dome are vertical, that is, in the direction of the meridians,

322

12.36 Shear mechanism in dome.

since the meridional arches are funiculars of the load; reactions in any other direction would produce bending moments in the dome (Fig. 12.35). In order to have a pure state of membrane stress in the shell, the boundary must be free to move outward, and the reactions must always act in the direction of the meridians. **In practice this is impossible.** A moving boundary would present practical difficulties and disadvantages; the reactions should rotate in order to remain tangent to the meridians if and when the boundary rotates because of the deformation of the shell under load (Fig. 12.34). In common practice, instead, the equator of the shell is reinforced by a stiff ring, which prevents almost entirely, the outward motion of the boundary and its rotation, and introduces an inward thrust and bending at the equator. The shell, which would open up at the equator under the membrane stresses induced by the load, develops a kink or sudden change in curvature and, hence, bending stresses around the boundary [Fig. 12.37(a)].

The **bending disturbance** thus introduced at the boundary does not penetrate deeply into the shell, but is limited to a narrow band in the neighborhood of the boundary. This "damping out" of boundary disturbances, another useful characteristic of thin shells, occurs because the bending displacements of the meridians, which could be large in view of the small bending rigidity of the shell, are restrained by the parallels. Large meridional displacements imply large changes in the radius of the parallels, and, hence, large tensile or compressive strains in the parallels. The parallels, instead, are stiff in tension and compression, and do not allow such large displacements; they permit a small amount of bulging in and out of the meridian and, hence, a small amount of bending, which peters out as one moves away from the shell boundary (Fig. 12.38).

324

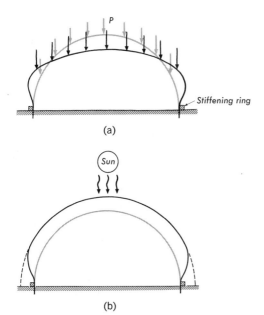

(a)

(b)

12.37 Bending deformations at ring-stiffened dome boundary.

12.38 Bending disturbance at dome boundary.

The width of the area affected by the bending boundary disturbance is proportional to the square root of the ratio of thickness to radius of the dome; in order to reduce the width of the disturbed zone the shell must be made thinner. For a thickness equal to one four-hundredth of the radius, the width of the disturbed zone is only one tenth of the radius (Fig. 12.38). Thus most of the shell is actually in a state of undisturbed membrane stress.

Bending disturbances, often more severe than those due to the loads, are produced by thermal conditions. When exposure to sun increases the shell temperature, the entire dome changes shape, uniformly increasing its radius [Fig. 12.37(b)]. If a ring prevents this boundary displacement, the shell once again presents a sudden change in curvature, and develops high bending stresses of the same nature as those discussed above. Since boundary displacements due to thermal changes are usually larger than those due to the loads, the bending stresses due to thermal expansion are usually larger than those due to the loads. If the temperature of a dome spanning 100 feet increases uniformly by 30 degrees Fahrenheit, the dome boundary displaces radially by one tenth of an inch. This displacement is three times larger than that produced by the dead load and a heavy snow load; hence the thermal bending stresses at the boundary are three times as large as those due to the loads.

Whenever the boundary reactions are not tangent to the meridians, bending stresses occur in the neighborhood of the boundary. Thus, if a dome is supported on evenly spaced columns rather than all around its boundary, the membrane stress pattern changes (Fig. 12.39), but, moreover, the columns introduce horizontal reactions at the dome boundary, and bending stresses are developed by the dome. Similarly, if portions of the dome are cut out by vertical or inclined planes and the dome rests on a few points, the support conditions differ substantially from those ideally required by membrane action, and bending stresses are to be expected. Moreover, any load capable of producing a kink or sudden change of curvature in a thin shell is bound to produce bending stresses: thus, concentrated loads cannot be carried by membrane stresses (Fig. 12.40). The thickness of the shell is often dictated by bending disturbances rather than by the membrane stresses due to the loads.

326

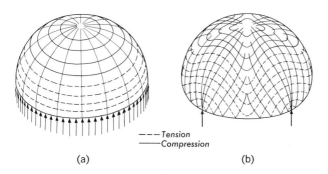

— — — Tension
——— Compression

(a)　　　　　　　　　　　　(b)

12.39 Principal stress lines of dome
under dead load.

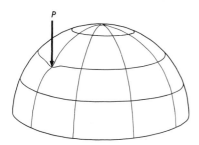

12.40 Concentrated load on thin shell.

Two additional conditions may call for a thickening of shells above the modest requirements of membrane stresses. One concerns reinforced-concrete shells and is of a purely practical character: enough thickness must be provided to cover the reinforcing bars on both the outside and the inside of the shell. The exact location of the bars in the shell thickness is a delicate and expensive matter; in countries with high labor costs it is often found less expensive to increase the shell thickness than to locate the steel carefully. Shells thinner than 2 or 3 inches are seldom economical in the United States, although 3/4 inch-thick shells have been competitively built; shells as thin as half an inch have been built in other countries.

Shells must often be thickened to prevent buckling. Any thin structural element subjected to compressive stresses may buckle, and thin shells are no exception. The buckling load for a thin-shell dome is proportional to the modulus of elasticity of the material and to the **square** of the thickness-to-radius ratio. With ratios often as small as $1/300$ or $1/400$, the buckling load may be exceptionally low. The buckling load for a dome 3 inches thick, spanning 100 feet, is about 150 pounds per square foot; with a factor of safety of 2½, the maximum load on the shell cannot exceed 60 pounds per square foot. This is equivalent to the dead load of the shell, including the roofing or insulating materials, and does not allow for any snow load. A shell of this sort could be built in the tropics, but not in the northern part of the United States.

328

The buckling resistance of a dome may be substantially increased, without increasing its thickness uniformly, by meridional and parallel ribs. This practice is well suited to the stiffening of steel domes, in which the thickness required by membrane stresses may be quite small in view of the tensile and compressive strength of the material. Concrete domes are seldom stiffened by ribs because of the cost of forms; the same result is achieved, sometimes, by undulations, which increase the cost of forms, but may also add to the appearance of the shell (Figs. 12.23–27).

A shell acts "properly" if it develops membrane stresses almost everywhere; it is then said to carry loads by **shell action.** It was shown above that the following three conditions must be satisfied for a dome to develop thin-shell action:

(1) The dome must be thin; it will thus be incapable of developing substantial bending action.

(2) It must be properly curved; it will thus be strong and stiff because of its form resistance.

(3) It must be properly supported; it will thus develop a small amount of bending in a limited portion of the shell.

These three conditions are essential to thin-shell action whatever the shape of the shell and the loads on it.

12.9 Membrane Action in Cylinders

Cylindrical or **barrel** shells are used to cover rectangular areas and are commonly supported on end frames, stiff in their own plane and flexible at right angles to it (Fig. 12.41). Their action may be considered as a combination of beam action in the longitudinal direction and a particular funicular-arch action in the transverse direction.

The longitudinal membrane stresses in a "long barrel"—a barrel in which the length is large in comparison with the width—are similar to those developed in a beam. The thin shell obtains its strength from its curved shape, and one may think of the barrel as a beam with a curved cross section. The longitudinal membrane stresses are linearly distributed across the depth of the barrel; the upper fibers are compressed, the lower fibers are tensioned (Fig. 12.42).

Beam action carries the load to the frames. These, because of their flexibility, cannot react longitudinally; the longitudinal stresses vanish at the end of the shell, just as they vanish at the end of a simply supported beam. The load is transferred to the end frames or **stiffeners** by shear action; tangential shears develop on the cylinder end sections, and their vertical components add up to the value of the load (Fig. 12.43). On the other hand, the action of the barrel differs slightly from beam action because the cross section of a beam is solid and indeformable, whereas the thin cross section of a shell deforms under load. If a thin, curved piece of material (paper or plastic) is supported on two grooved stiffeners, and loaded, the longitudinal boundaries of the cylinder will be seen to move **inward,** indicating the absence of the outward thrust typical of arch action, and showing the deformability of the cross section.

330

12.41 Barrel shell on end stiffeners.

12.42 Beam stresses in long barrels.

12.43 Shear reactions on barrel ends.

As the barrel becomes shorter, the influence of the deformability of its cross section is more felt, and the longitudinal stresses deviate from the straight-line, beam distribution. There comes a point where the stresses acquire the curved distribution of Fig. 12.44(a), in which both the top and bottom shell fibers are in tension, while the intermediate fibers are in compression. If the cross section of the barrel is prevented from deforming, either by intermediate stiffeners or by the continuity with adjacent barrels, the stress distribution becomes linear once again, indicating a return to the beam behavior of Fig. 12.44(b).

12.10 Bending Stresses in Cylinders

As the barrel becomes shorter, arch action and eventually plate action become preponderant. One may visualize the behavior of short barrels as due to the action of arches supported by longitudinal beams consisting of barrel strips near the boundaries (Fig. 12.45). Transverse, compressive arch stresses develop in the upper part of the barrel, petering out towards its longitudinal edges.

The compressive arch stresses introduce bending in the neighborhood of the barrel stiffeners. The arch compression produces a shortening of the transverse fibers of the barrel, and an inward displacement of the barrel section

(a)

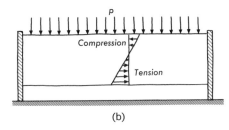

(b)

12.44 Longitudinal stresses in long and in short barrels.

(a)

(b)

12.45 Short-barrel action.

(Fig. 12.46). This displacement takes place freely at midspan, but at the barrel ends it is prevented by the stiffeners, which are rigid in their own plane. In order to restrain the inward displacement at the stiffener, while allowing it at midspan, the shell must bend; thus it develops some bending stresses at the stiffener (Fig. 12.46). This bending disturbance is of the same kind as that encountered at the boundary of a circular dome when its outward displacement is prevented by a stiff ring. The bending disturbance at the stiffeners peters out rapidly and is felt only a short distance. The width of the transverse band affected by the bending disturbance depends again on the square root of the thickness-to-radius ratio; the bending displacements bulge in and out and are rapidly "damped." The bending stresses at the stiffener edges are often absorbed by a local increase in the shell thickness.

The disturbed area at the end stiffeners is narrow **in comparison with the shell radius,** in any thin barrel. When the barrel is long—that is, when its length is substantially greater than its radius—only a small fraction of its **length** is under bending stresses [Fig. 12.47(a)]. But when the barrel is short —that is, when the barrel length is **less** than the radius—the width of the bending-stress area, even if small compared to the radius, may become large compared to the length of the barrel [Fig. 12.47(b)]. Thus, in short barrels the bending disturbance may affect a large portion of the total shell area. This result could be foreseen intuitively: in short barrels the load is carried directly to the stiffeners by the bending action of longitudinal shell strips, because the thickness of the shell may be small relative to the radius, but is large compared to the short span. Actually, since the short barrel is a two-dimensional resisting structure, it acts very much like a plate in carrying the load directly to the two stiffeners, and necessarily develops bending stresses over most of its surface.

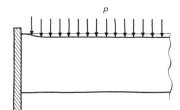

12.46 Bending at barrel stiffener.

(a)

(b)

12.47 Bending in long and short barrels.

Thermal displacements and shrinkage of the concrete during setting may produce bending disturbances at the stiffeners substantially greater than those produced by the loads. They often dictate the increase in thickness at the stiffeners' edge.

How essential it is for a shell to be "properly supported" in order to develop only membrane stresses is clearly shown by barrel shells. A long barrel, supported on end stiffeners, carries loads by longitudinal tensile and compressive stresses and transverse shears, that is, by beam action (Fig. 12.42). The same barrel, supported along its longitudinal edges, develops essentially arch action, since each transverse strip may be considered as an arch supported at its ends and capable of developing the necessary thrust (Fig. 12.48). If the shape of the cylinder section is the funicular of the loads, each strip will develop only compressive transverse stresses and no longitudinal stresses. This is also a membrane state of stress, but totally different from that developed by the stiffener-supported barrel, which consists essentially of longitudinal stresses. If the barrel cross section is not the funicular of the loads, bending stresses will develop in the arched strips (see Section 6.3); these bending stresses do not have the character of boundary disturbances, but pervade the entire shell. Although a stiffener-supported barrel may be very thin, a barrel supported on its longitudinal edges and acting as a **vault** must be thick to resist the bending stresses in the arched strips.

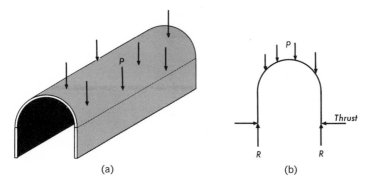

(a)

(b)

12.48 Barrel acting as vault.

The stiffener-supported barrel also develops some boundary disturbances along its longitudinal, free edges. These are minor disturbances, but have a tendency to penetrate **more** into the shell than the disturbances along the stiffener boundaries. It is not difficult to realize why. If one bends the edge of a thin plate, one must apply an equal and opposite bending action to the opposite edge in order to equilibrate it. The plate bends **all over,** and transfers the bending action from one edge to the other, unchanged (Fig. 12.49). If the thin plate is curved into a cylinder, bending applied at one of its curved boundaries is **not** transmitted to the opposite boundary, but dies out quickly [Fig. 12.50(a)]. It is thus seen that the curvature acquired by the plate "damps out" bending **in a direction at right angles to the curvature.** The bending disturbance at the stiffener ends of the barrel is damped out **rapidly** by the cylinder curvature at right angles to it. A curvature **in the direction of the bending disturbance** produces a lesser amount of damping, so that a longitudinal-edge disturbance dies out slowly, although usually it is not transmitted all the way to the other longitudinal edge [Fig. 12.50(b)]. The longitudinal-edge disturbance in the barrel is dampened less rapidly than in a plate curved at right angles to the disturbance; the width of the disturbed band along the longitudinal edges is about twice as large as along the curved boundary, for most shells.

338

12.49 Bending of flat plate.

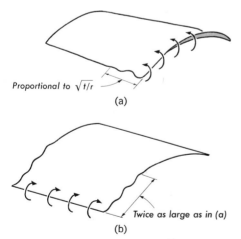

Proportional to $\sqrt{t/r}$

(a)

Twice as large as in (a)

(b)

12.50 Boundary bending of curved plate.

Barrel shells are not as stiff as domes, since their single curvature makes them behave very much like beams. Whenever it is necessary to increase their stiffness, it is customary to add longitudinal beams along their edges. This adds area on the tensile side of the cross section, so that a larger part of the barrel shell is under compression and the tensile stresses are absorbed mostly by the edge beams, acting as flanges. The edge beams, moreover, are used to absorb longitudinal shears developing at the edge of the shell, which introduce tension in the boundary beams (Fig. 12.51).

Just as the upper flange of an I-beam may buckle in compression, the upper fibers of a long barrel shell may buckle under longitudinal compression. The resistance of long barrel shells to buckling is higher than that of domes, since compressive stresses are developed essentially only in a portion of the shell and only in one direction. The buckling load is proportional to the modulus of elasticity of the material, and to the thickness-to-radius ratio rather than to its square, as in the case of domes. Notwithstanding the greater buckling strength of long barrel shells, the danger of buckling may often demand an increase in the barrel thickness above the value required by a state of membrane stress.

Whenever the thickness required to avoid buckling makes the bending resistance of the shell so large as to reduce its membrane action, it becomes more economical to rib the shell transversely (Fig. 12.52). Stiffeners are commonly used in steel shells; they are used less often in concrete shells because they increase the cost of forms.

340

(a)

(b)

12.51 Shears on longitudinal boundary beams.

12.52 Ribbed barrel.

12.11 Stresses in Synclastic Translational Shells

A variety of curves may be used to generate translational shells with double positive curvature; arcs of circles and arcs of parabolas are the most common among them. Translational shells are supported by shear stresses on boundary arches, just as barrels are supported by shear on end stiffeners (Fig. 12.53). The supporting arches are rigid in their own plane and flexible at right angles to them, so that compression or tension perpendicular to the arches is not developed at the shell boundary. The action of translational shells may be considered as barrel action in two directions, since the shells have curvature in two directions, but the central portion of the shells acts very much like a shallow dome, and develops compressive stresses along both the meridians and the parallels. The portion of the shell near the supporting arches develops a certain amount of bending disturbances, and although they peter out rapidly into the shell in view of the curvature at right angles to it, a thickening of the shell is often required at the boundary.

Some elliptic paraboloidal shells are built of hollow tile and concrete, with a minimal amount of reinforcing steel (0.6 pounds per square foot), on a movable form a few feet wide, shaped as one of the two generating curves and sliding on wooden arches having the shape of the other generating curve (Fig. 12.54). The shell is built in slices, which act as separate arches until they are made monolithic by pouring of concrete over the entire surface. These are among the few thin shells ever tested under total and partial loads. The tests proved that all the basic assumptions made about their action are satisfied in practice. The bending disturbance at the boundary penetrates only for a short distance into the shell; the shell does not thrust out and is supported exclusively by boundary shears. The rigidity of the shell proved to be exceptionally high: under a uniform load of 30 pounds per square foot over its entire surface, a 60-by-90 foot shell presented a top deflection of less than one eighth of an inch, or a span-to-deflection ratio of 9000.

342

12.53 Boundary shears in translational shell.

12.54 Tile and concrete elliptic paraboloid.

12.12 Saddle-Shell Action

The behavior of the most common saddle shell, the hyperbolic paraboloid, shows the dependence of its structural action on support conditions. This surface was shown in Section 12.4 to be generated either by a vertical parabola with downward curvature sliding on a vertical parabola with upward curvature, or by a straight-line segment the ends of which slide on two straight lines askew in space (Figs. 12.15, 12.16).

When the shell is supported on two parabolic arches or stiffeners, it transfers the load to the support by shears (Fig. 12.55). Its action is similar to that of a stiffener-supported barrel, but the upward curvature in the longitudinal direction gives the shell additional strength, particularly **against buckling.** If the shell tends to buckle, the parabolas with downward curvature must flatten; this deformation is resisted by the parabolas with upward curvature, since the tensile stresses in these stabilize the compressive stresses in the others.

If the paraboloid reaches the ground, its intersections with the ground consist of two outward-curved boundaries (the two branches of a hyperbola), so that the area covered by the shell has two straight sides and two curved sides (Fig. 12.55). When the paraboloid does not reach the ground, the shell may be supported on four corners, but the end stiffeners must then carry the vertical and horizontal loads on the shell as two hinged arches. Bending disturbances, similar to those at the curved boundaries of barrels, are encountered at the intersection of the paraboloid with the stiffeners. Their values and the width of the disturbed band are of the same magnitude as those in cylindrical shells.

When the hyperbolic paraboloid is supported on its straight-line generatrices, the directions of principal stress are those of the parabolas (Fig. 12.6). Tension along the upward parabolas combines with compression along the downward parabolas to create a state of pure shear along the straight lines

344

12.55 Hyperbolic paraboloid supported on end stiffeners.

(Fig. 12.56). The load is thus carried to the supporting boundaries by pure shear directed along the straight lines, and these shears accumulate along the boundary supports (Fig. 12.57). The supporting elements are usually "beams," but these elements, rather than by vertical loads, are loaded by the shears accumulating along their lengths, so that they behave like compressive struts or tensile bars, except for the action of their own dead load.

When the hyperbolic paraboloid is shallow, the **principal** membrane stresses are **identical** tensions and compressions producing shears of the same intensity (Fig. 12.56). These stresses have the same value **all over the shell.** Moreover, since membrane stresses are uniformly distributed across the depth of the shell, the hyperbolic paraboloid may be said to have a 100 per cent over-all efficiency; the material of the shell is equally stressed **at any point of any cross section.** The membrane stresses in the paraboloid are proportional to the total uniform load on it, and inversely proportional to the shell rise and the shell thickness. The shell rise should not be less than one-sixth to one-tenth the span in order to avoid high compressive stresses, which may buckle the shell.

It may be proved that the membrane stresses considered above arise in the hyperbolic paraboloid **only if** its straight-line boundary stiffeners are very rigid vertically, and very flexible horizontally. Such conditions are seldom encountered in practice. If, for example, the boundary stiffeners are cantilevered from the two low points of the shell (Fig. 12.56), the boundary of the shell is not rigidly supported, as required by the theoretical assumptions. Actually, some of the stiffeners' weight hangs from the shell, and the two halves of the paraboloid behave very much like cantilevered beams with the variable, curved cross section of the downward parabolas.

Boundary disturbances are always present at the intersection with the boundary stiffeners; they penetrate into the shell more than the disturbances at the curved boundary of a cylinder, but less than those encountered along a cylindrical straight boundary.

346

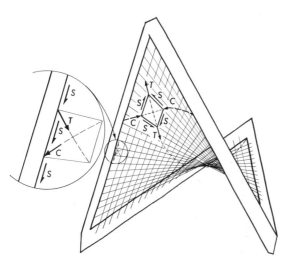

12.56 Hyperbolic paraboloid supported on straight generatrices.

Roofs are usually built by combinations of hyperbolic paraboloid segments. One of the most commonly used involves four segments, the outer corners of which are supported on columns (Fig. 12.57). In this case, the inclined outer stiffeners and the horizontal inner stiffeners are all compressed by the accumulation of boundary shears (Fig. 12.57). The thrust of the inclined outer stiffeners is absorbed by tie-rods, while the inner beams are in equilibrium under the equal and opposite compressions of each pair of paraboloidal segments (Fig. 12.57). The roof has the appearance of a regular gabled roof, and its action at the corners is purely vertical, once the tie-rods are tensioned.

The same combination of four segments may be used as an umbrella and supported on a central column (Fig. 12.58). In this case, the outer horizontal stiffeners are tensioned by the accumulation of shears, and the tension in one of them balances the tension in the stiffener of the adjoining segment. The roof is innerly equilibrated and does not require tie-rods (Fig. 12.58). In either combination, the weight of the horizontal stiffeners (the boundary stiffeners for the umbrella, and the inner cross for the gabled roof) is carried by the shell itself; the shell therefore, develops some bending stresses. It may also buckle in the central region where it is flat—that is, where no appreciable curvature is present to help carry the loads by membrane stresses.

A variety of other combinations of hyperbolic paraboloids may be used to cover areas of varied shape. Each one of these combinations must be carefully analyzed to determine whether it is innerly balanced. A typically unbalanced combination consists of two segments, used as a north-light roof (Fig. 12.29). The thrust of the inclined boundary struts is equilibrated by a tie-rod, but the two compressive forces accumulated along the inclined strut common to the two segments are not equilibrated (Fig. 12.59). Hence, the horizontal boundary beam is acted upon by a concentrated load at midspan and is subject to bending. The shell behavior, in this case, is a bending action in horizontal projection, with compression at the upper boundary and tension at the lower boundary, due to a load concentrated at midspan; the two tensile forces at the outer lateral boundary of the shell equilibrate the concentrated load, just like beam reactions (Fig. 12.59).

348

12.57 Hyperbolic paraboloid roof supported on outer columns.

12.58 Boundary shears on hyperbolic paraboloid umbrella.

12.59 Shears on boundary beams of hyperbolic paraboloidal conoid.

Hyperbolic paraboloids have also been used as elements of roofs with a very high rise, or as almost vertical elements. In such cases their behavior is totally different from that of the shallow paraboloids considered above, and similar to the behavior of a thin plate loaded in its own plane. It may be often approximated by the behavior of deep beams (see Section 7.1).

The different mechanisms by which the hyperbolic paraboloid carries loads are one more example of the dependence of shell behavior on support conditions.

12.13 Scalloped and Other Types of Shells

Interesting shell shapes may be obtained by adding local curvatures to a simple surface, according to structural needs or esthetic requirements.

An elliptic paraboloid intersected by a horizontal plane is a smooth surface covering an elliptic area. In order to enhance its appearance and stiffen its boundary, it may be scalloped, thus creating local curvatures that peter out towards the interior of the shell (Fig. 12.25). The introduction of such curvatures substantially changes the shell behavior. The smooth paraboloid carries load by stresses similar to those encountered in a rotational shell: compression along the meridians, and compression or tension along the

350

elliptical parallels. The introduction of local curvatures destroys the stiffness typical of membrane behavior. Under the action of loads the shell tends to open up, since its undulated parallels cannot develop the hoop stresses that play such an important role in stiffening rotational shells. The action of the shell is similar to that of a series of arches with variable cross section, hinged at the supports and at the crown, where the lack of curvature reduces the bending resistance of the shell (see Section 8.5). Circular domes of large diameter have also been built by scalloping a spherical surface with the purpose of increasing its buckling resistance (Fig. 12.27). The waving of the parallels very much reduces their stiffening action; such shells behave as a series of arches crossing at the top of the dome and hinged there.

The membrane stresses of conoidal shells also depend on support conditions. If the straight boundaries are supported vertically and connected by tie-rods, each slice of the shell acts as a tied arch, and substantial bending stresses are to be expected for all loads for which the cross section of the shell is not a funicular curve. When the longitudinal boundaries are not supported, the conoid behaves as a cylinder with a variable rise, and develops bending stresses in the neighborhood of the end arches only. If such a shell is scalloped, the transverse arch action is destroyed, since the conoid tends to open up; in order to restore its rigidity, the undulations must be stiffened by transverse stiffeners at regular intervals.

North-light roofs for industrial buildings are economically built by means of thin shells. Their structural behavior is similar to that of a beam with a shallow, curved cross section, whose neutral axis is not horizontal, but inclined towards the upper shell boundary (Fig. 12.60). The shell fibers above the inclined neutral axis are compressed and those below are tensioned. When the beam stiffening the shell at its upper boundary is large, the neutral axis may cross it, and the fibers of the shell may be mostly in tension (Fig. 12.60).

Some of the largest thin shells in the world have been built to resist horizontal rather than vertical loads. Retaining walls loaded by the thrust of the earth may be built as vertical cylinders or conoids (Fig. 12.61). Cylindrical tanks containing water, oil, or other liquids are built as thin concrete shells to resist the outward pressure of the liquid. Dams, up to a height of 800 feet, have been built with curvatures both in the vertical and the horizontal

352

12.60 Cross section of north-light barrel shell.

p

12.61 Conoidal retaining wall.

sections and a thickness of only a few feet (Fig. 12.62). The ratio of radius of curvature to thickness in these dams is of the order of 400 or more, so that such shells are to be considered thin even though they may be several feet thick at their foot.

It is almost impossible to mention all the shapes used in thin-shell design, much less to consider all the combinations of shapes that conceivably could be used; the esthetic, architectural, and structural possibilities of this kind of construction are practically unlimited.

12.14 Thin-Shell Construction Problems

The exceptional structural efficiency of thin shells would make their use even more popular, if they did not present a number of practical problems, a few of which will be mentioned here.

The problem of forming curved surfaces for reinforced-concrete shells has, for a time, made their use uneconomical in countries with high labor costs. The forming problem may be reduced in a variety of ways. Roofs in which the same element appears repeatedly are built by pouring each element on a form, which is then shifted a few days or only a few hours later. Prefabrication of the shell elements and their erection on a reduced scaffolding has become a standard procedure in which expensive forms are eliminated. The joining of the prefabricated elements is carried out with great care, and often requires welding the reinforcing bars sticking out of the elements, and pouring the joints at a later date. Most of the exceptional structures designed by Nervi are built by this procedure.

354

12.62 Thin-shell dam.

The use of a concrete gun allows the spraying of layers of concrete (Shot-concrete or Gunite) on the reinforcing bars with a minor amount of formwork. In certain cases the bars are hung from boundary stiffeners; in other cases, they are supported by a simple scaffolding, in which the insulation panels constitute the actual shell surface against which the concrete is shot. Finally, inflatable balloons have been used as forms to support the steel and against which to spray the concrete (see Section 11.1).

Prefabrication of shells by elements is often used in conjunction with post-tensioning. It was observed in previous sections that certain types of shells develop tensile stresses over large portions of their area. These tensile stresses may be eliminated by introducing in the thickness of the shell steel cables or **tendons** which are tensioned after the concrete has hardened; they compress the shell so as to altogether eliminate the tensile stresses due to the load (see Section 3.3). The thin shells of cylindrical tanks are usually post-tensioned by spirals of steel, thus guaranteeing the waterproofness of the tanks under all conditions. North-light shells with large spans may also be post-tensioned by curved tendons so as to eliminate tensile stresses in the shell portions below the inclined neutral axis (Fig. 12.60).

The problem of weatherproofing curved roofs has been completely solved in recent years by the development of plastic paints, which may be either sprayed or rolled in extremely thin layers. Such paints are usually transparent, and may be colored so as to add to the appearance of the roof.

Curved surfaces present acoustical difficulties, particularly if large, smooth, and hard. In such cases acoustical insulation may be attached to or sprayed

356

on the inner surface of the shell, or used on the floor of the area covered by the shell. It is now possible to forecast with accuracy the acoustical behavior of large shells by means of preliminary analytical or model studies of their surface properties. Acoustical problems may thus be eliminated before the shell is built, which is more economical than doing so afterward.

Thermal problems are eased by the use of insulating materials applied either to the interior or to the exterior of the shell; in the second case they are usually sprayed over with concrete. Appropriate air circulation inside the shell helps eliminate condensation.

The architect must be aware of people's responses to thin-shell roofs. A smooth, large surface with a uniform curvature, such as a sphere, lacks a dimensional reference; it does not relate to the human being, unless visual elements are introduced for this purpose. Thus, a relatively small spherical roof may loom large overhead, but may also give a feeling of confinement unless properly articulated. On the other hand, repeated elements with small curvature, such as cylinders, are more easily encompassed by the human eye, and give a feeling of protection without confinement. Conoids give a feeling of protection, and at the same time let the outside visually enter the covered area from one direction. Hyperbolic paraboloids supported on their low points seem to be projected indefinitely into the sky, because of their upward slope in the direction of their high points, but give a feeling of protection in a perpendicular direction.

The proper shell form to be chosen by the architect depends, therefore, on a large number of factors: economical, constructional, structural, esthetic, and even psychological. Only by satisfying all these requirements can he achieve a successful shell design.

Chapter Thirteen

Conclusion

13.1 Intuition and Knowledge

The preceding chapters have attempted a **qualitative** presentation of structural concepts on the basis of general experience with forces, materials, and deformations. A casual reading of the foregoing pages may illuminate the structural actions most commonly encountered in architecture; a careful reading may clarify, in addition, more sophisticated types of structural behavior, seldom considered by the layman. In any case, the purely intuitive approach used to introduce these concepts cannot be expected to lead to **quantitative** knowledge in a field as complex as structures. For this, an analytical, mathematical presentation is needed, of the kind required for an understanding of any branch of physics.

Intuition is an essentially synthetic process which brings about the sudden, direct understanding of ideas more or less consciously analyzed over a period of time. It becomes a satisfactory road to knowledge on two conditions: it should be based on a large amount of prior experience, and it should be verified with great care.

Intuition may be greatly refined by practice. One of the best tools for refining structural intuition is a laboratory where the diversified actions considered in this book may be demonstrated. Since all structural actions involve motions, and motions are the visual result of these actions, models are ideally suited for the intuitive presentation of structural concepts. For this reason the reader has often been invited to build elementary models, which demonstrate the structural behavior of simple elements more convincingly than any drawing ever will.

On the other hand, it cannot be overemphasized that intuition without experience is a dangerous tool, since its suggestions cannot be gauged. The reader should be wary of what he "seems to feel should happen" in a given physical situation, and, in particular, of the geometrical aspect of a structure. It is hard to believe, at first, that the straight sides of a cylindrical barrel move inwards under load, because the curved section of the cylinder suggests arch action, and arches are **"known"** to push outwards.

13.2 Qualitative and Quantitative Knowledge

Qualitative knowledge should often be a prerequisite to quantitative study, since interest in a field is seldom aroused without some prior understanding. It is hoped that the reader with an interest in structures may obtain from the preceding chapters that minimum understanding of structural behavior required to arouse his interest, and to lead him to a serious study of the subject.

Structures are best presented in the language proper to the quantitative analysis of measurable facts: mathematics; not the complex mathematics required for an understanding of the more advanced aspects of science, but the simple mathematics of numbers, algebra, and elementary calculus. No **thorough knowledge** of structures may be acquired **without** the use of these **mathematical tools.** Mathematics does not explain physical behavior; it just describes it. But mathematical descriptions are so efficient that an elementary formula may clearly and simply express ideas that in verbal form would require pages.

The availability of structural knowledge, made possible by the use of mathematics, has produced impressive results. Structures that in the past could have been conceived and built only by architectural geniuses, are designed, at present, by modest engineers in the routine of their office work. This democratization of structural knowledge, while putting advanced structures within the reach of the average architect, introduces the danger of architectural misuse by the practitioner who lacks a solid structural foundation.

There is little doubt in the minds of both engineers and architects that modern structural concepts are used properly only when the architect has a thorough understanding of structures. This does not imply that all architects should become mathematicians; it simply suggests that those practitioners who wish to express themselves through structural forms should first be able to use the tools of quantitative analysis. They will be amazed to find, later on, that their cultivated intuition will often reach "correct" structural solutions without too many mathematical manipulations.

The field of structures is evolving rapidly under the pressure of growing needs. The structuralist and the architect must strive, by all means at their disposal, toward a better understanding and a more fruitful collaboration. May the technician serve the artist to the greater glory of the only technological art: the art of architecture.

Index

364